THE ADVENTURES OF LI CHI

Humphrey Evans

The Adventures of
LI CHI

A Modern Chinese Legend

E. P. Dutton & Co., Inc.

New York   1967

In reality, there is no such thing as art for art's sake, art that stands above the classes or art that runs parallel to or remains independent of politics.—MAO TSE-TUNG

Contents

⊌⊌⊌⊌⊌⊌⊌⊌⊌

Foreword

In a 1962 interview with a Chinese Communist defector, I learned that the Peking government attempts to hide from its people the fact that it has to purchase grain from capitalist countries, particularly from Canada. The defector added, however, that the people know about the purchases even though they are forced to maintain the pretense that the superior foreign grain is a home-grown socialist product.

I asked how the Chinese felt about this situation. The defector shrugged, but then smiled. "A friend of my uncle in Wuhu dared express what I suppose we all felt," he said. "At a political discussion meeting there, he was ordered to explain the thought of Mao Tse-tung as it applied to agriculture. My uncle's friend answered, 'Chairman Mao is history's greatest agricultural genius; he has demonstrated that wheat can be sown in North China and reaped in North America.'"

I could hardly believe that anyone in Communist China had the courage to ridicule the regime so cuttingly in public. Nevertheless, the refugee insisted that the story was true. He said that his uncle's friend, whose name was Li Chi, was probably the only man on the China mainland who had nothing to fear from the Communists.

Since then I have listened to many stories about Li Chi. Most of the present refugees from Communist China have heard of him, or of someone like him. A few even claim to have been Li Chi's friend.

Nevertheless, the Li Chi of these stories does not really exist. He is pure myth. True, some of the biographical details ascribed to him were taken from certain living persons. Also, there is in Peking a man named Li Chi who, like our hero, is an artist, but nothing else in that man's background or personality is the same. The Chinese characters for our Li Chi are written so as to imply that he is funny-peculiar, an oddball—something, perhaps, like our beatniks.

Our hero may be only fiction, but the stories about him are of a consistent type and are instantly recognizable. A common denominator in the stories is Li Chi's indestructibility. Despite an unceasing effort in Communist China to stamp out individualism, Li Chi is shown as managing not only to maintain his individuality but actually to thrive. An important detail about his life story is that he is never made to join the Communist Party, although if he were a real person the pressure on him to do so would be powerful. Instead, Li Chi exploits the exploiters; he is always on the side of the masses, against the authorities. He demonstrates, in a modern idealized form, the ancient Chinese ability to survive.

In a long and turbulent history, the Chinese people have developed their own techniques for coping with tribulation, whether man-made or natural. The techniques are demonstrated over and over again in the classical literature concerning the legendary heroes. Unquestionably, Li Chi is in the process of joining that group. The fact that he is still supposed to be living is the only real difference between him and the ancient heroes.

Perhaps, however, he is fated never to die, but rather to fade away and be forgotten when the need for him has finally dissolved.

Li Chi is needed in the same way that myths have always been needed. He softens reality into a more acceptable form. He simplifies issues. He is proof that the forces of oppression are not omnipotent. Above all, he is every man's idealized image of himself; he always says and does what we would like to say and do, if we had the necessary courage and wit. In a society that attempts to suppress self-expression, the existence of someone like Li Chi is the very meaning of hope.

Li Chi may be a myth, but in a sense he has more reality than most living persons. A number of people *believe* that he lives, and they have supplied him with a detailed background. Moreover, when the stories about him are arranged in chronological order a picture of a seemingly genuine person emerges.

I admit, however, that some facets of his personality appear inconsistent or out of character—at least to Westerners. For example, many anecdotes about him imply that he is somewhat scatterbrained. Thus, on a trip, he may forget his food coupons; rather than make an issue of his carelessness he uncomplainingly goes without eating. To the Chinese, apparently, this characteristic makes him wistfully appealing. To us, however, it does not seem to fit with his cunning and his skill with intrigue.

Others have begun to collect and compare Li Chi stories. We form a small group, here and in Hong Kong, and we get the material from interviews with refugees from the China mainland. We often hear the same story from several different sources—a fact that indicates that these stories are well circulated in China. Even the accounts of Li Chi's early life are generally consistent, and they are detailed enough to suggest that some unknown real person was used as a model.

Li Chi is said to have been born in Anhwei Province in 1939. He must have been an unattractive infant because, as an adult, he is described as "undersized and scrawny." His face is said to have a pushed-in look. His mouth is crooked and too wide. His ears, hands, and feet are ludicrously large.

Even if he had been a perfect specimen, however, it is not likely that Li Chi would have been welcomed into his family. His parents were landless peasants, and so poor that they had no hope of bettering their lot. Moreover, they already had a son, who would inherit the father's few possessions, and two daughters for whom husbands would need to be found. Li Chi, therefore, represented only another mouth to feed, and no note of joy attended his arrival.

Li Chi probably fought hard for survival from the moment he was born. He learned early to make up for his deficiencies: despite his small stature, he developed a wiry strength. Charm, wit, and shrewdness became compensations for his ugliness. At the age of six, with these achievements, he was adopted by a small landowner in a neighboring area; the man had produced only daughters, and he planned to raise Li Chi to be the husband of one of them.

The farmer subjected Li Chi to long hours of hard labor, but otherwise seems to have treated the boy well enough. Also, he arranged for Li Chi to be given primary schooling. Li Chi had sense enough to realize that an education would be an asset, and he applied himself diligently.

In his schoolwork, his most noticeable aptitude was the ease with which he memorized characters and learned to write them well. This obviously was meant to indicate a natural artistic talent. During this period he began to draw. He used pieces of charcoal mostly, and he covered every scrap of paper he could find, and even bare walls, with sketches of people and animals. He often used caricature, and proved that his wit and perception were sharp.

Li Chi was eleven years old when the Communists took over the mainland in 1949. Little revolutionary effort was wasted on the area in which Li Chi was living, and he knew nothing about the change of regimes until the land-reform program in 1950. One day, suddenly, the farmer told Li Chi to return to his parents. Thereupon, the farmer and his family left hurriedly for Taiwan.

In his home area, Li Chi found much excitement and turmoil. The land reform there was already under way. The Communists were liquidating the current landowners and redistributing the land. To Li Chi's surprise, his parents became the owners of a small farm. He was even more surprised to find, however, that his parents were not entirely happy about their good fortune.

The reason for this was an aspect of the fact that in Li Chi's part of Anhwei only a small percentage of the land was held by absentee owners. In these few cases the land was simply appropriated and distributed among landless peasants; no concern was wasted on the distant owner. Most of the local land, however, was held by small farmers who were only slightly better off than the landless peasants. Nevertheless, the Communists insisted that these farmers were guilty of the unforgivable crime of being landowners. Most of them were "struggled against." They were hauled up before crowds of assembled peasants who, on the threat of being struggled against themselves, were made to accuse the farmers, usually falsely, of other crimes. Thereupon, in response to the "will of the masses," the Communists either shot the accused farmers on the spot or sent them to labor reform to die more slowly. The farms, then, were turned over to the landless.

Few of the landless in Li Chi's district had any real objection to this procedure. Certainly they were cooperating with the Communists in the liquidation of the farmers. A man who obtains his neighbor's property by falsely accusing his neighbor, however, does not easily convince himself that he has acted with honesty and virtue. Moreover, he is not likely to have much regard for the morality and integrity of the authorities who were pushing him to acquire property by such means. And, finally, he is not likely to feel secure in his new position as a landowner;

after all, it was being made only too clear that, from the Communist viewpoint, private ownership of land was a crime for which one death was inadequate penalty. Thus, the thought was inescapable that sooner or later the Communists would turn on the new landlords.

Understandably, Li Chi's parents and neighbors had doubts about the land-reform program, even though they were cooperating with it. They were worried and frightened. Also, they were deeply suspicious of the outsiders—city-bred intellectuals with no real knowledge of peasant problems—who had been sent by the authorities to implement the program.

These were the circumstances, according to the legend, under which the twelve-year-old Li Chi first became aware of the new regime, and pitted his cunning against the craftiness of the Party cadres.

THE ADVENTURES OF LI CHI

CHAPTER I

The Beginning

Li Chi's first conflict with the regime arose over two pictures he drew.

When he returned to his own family's village, no one there knew about his talent. He himself said nothing about it simply because he did not know that his ability to draw was noteworthy. He was the sort of scrawny child whom adults rarely even noticed.

Nevertheless, his understanding of adults and their relationships was precocious. Before long he knew an extraordinary amount about everyone in the village. Like a child, however, he judged people by his own standards, and the people he admired were not often those whom the adults respected most.

For example, Li Chi had the most respect for the old fortune-teller. The man was so feeble with age that he could not leave his hut, but Li Chi regarded him as the wisest man on earth.

When the land-reform cadres had arrived, however, the fortune-teller's prediction was, "The Communists will bring suffering here, but only when the village brook runs red will you rise

17

up and drive them out." This angered the cadres, and only the fortune-teller's age prevented him from being declared a counterrevolutionary. Instead, the cadres jeered at him for being a superstitious old fool, and they made the other villagers do the same.

Conversely, Comrade Pu who led the jeering (and the group of cadres) did not know the difference between rice and barley or between a bull and a cow. Moreover, he was almost blind without his thick glasses, and he was so small and skinny that anyone over fifteen in the village could thrash him. Thus Li Chi was contemptuous of the head cadre, and he looked down upon his fellow villagers who looked up to Comrade Pu with so much deference.

Li Chi enjoyed looking at Mrs. Chuan the most. She was big and slightly cross-eyed, but she was nicely rounded and warmhearted. Her husband, the village repairman, was twice her age, half her size, and walked with his knees bent.* For these reasons, the villagers, particularly the men, were nice to her. Besides his mother, Mrs. Chuan was the only other person who ever noticed Li Chi. Other women said that Mrs. Chuan noticed only goats—whether old or young—that had three legs, two short and one long, but Li Chi loved her

The villager whom Li Chi loved the least was a big brutish young man named Meng. Even as a child he had been sullen, and he had grown up to be bitter and resentful.

The first question the cadres had asked upon arriving in the village was, "Who here hates the landowners most?" The villagers agreed that the answer probably was Meng. True, Meng did hate the landowners, but he also hated the landless. The cadres did not understand this, and they made him the local "hero of the land-reform movement."

Meng had been ingenious at bringing false charges against the landowners, and ferocious in helping to liquidate them. For this,

* In many parts of the Orient, to say that a man "walks with his knees bent" is to imply that he is impotent.

18

he was made a Party member, and his authority was second only to Comrade Pu's. Meng now devised countless ways of exploiting his authority. No one in the village escaped his "squeeze," and no one dared complain to the cadres about it Animal instinct made Li Chi keep out of Meng's sight.

Because Meng and the cadres commandeered in the name of "the people" anything they wanted, the villagers soon possessed nothing but the bare necessities. Thus Li Chi, for the first time, found himself without any drawing materials, not even charcoal and old newsprint. In desperation, he took his problem to the fortune-teller.

The old man seemed to listen, but he did not reply. He sat with his eyes closed, muttering to himself, while his mummified head shook with palsy. Li Chi waited respectfully, but was about to give up when the old man spoke. "Long ago, this place was famous for a certain indelible dye," he said in his high shaky voice, "but the people have forgotten how to make it." He lapsed again into unintelligible muttering, but now Li Chi waited patiently.

"Follow the village brook upstream for almost a *li*," the old man said finally. "Find some bushes with brownish-red berries. Make some red clay pots and cook the berries in them with water and cow's urine. Let the mixture stand half a day." The old man opened his eyes and held up an admonishing finger. "But keep this a secret," he said, "or those outsiders will take your dye and not let you have the berries." Then some wheezy cackling sounds bubbled up in the old man's throat; Li Chi realized with surprise that the old man was laughing.

Even in broad daylight, Li Chi could filter through the village without being seen. He pushed through the vegetation along the banks of the brook and found the bushes with berries. He had difficulty in making containers from the brook's red clay, but he finally managed it. By early afternoon he had five large pots of a thin, stinking brown mash brewed according to the fortune-teller's directions. Li Chi was disappointed because he could not

19

imagine the mash becoming a dye. He remembered, however, that the mixture was to stand for half a day. Thus he hid the pots and made his way back to the village.

In bed that night, the prospect of being able to paint again excited him so much that he stayed awake to plan what he would draw. At midnight, a full moon came up. On impulse, he decided to check on what was happening to his dye. He slipped out of his quilt, retrieved an old jar that he had previously found and hidden, and again moved silently through the village. The moonlight was bright enough so that he made his way easily up along the brook.

To his delight, he found that the sediment in his mixture had settled, leaving a bright crimson fluid. He dipped his jar into it. Next he found some soft twigs of varying thicknesses; he pulped the ends with a rock to make a set of brushes. Now all he needed was something to paint on.

Back in the village, he searched the places where trash might be thrown. He hoped to find old pieces of cardboard or newspaper, or perhaps some rags that could be washed out and stretched on a board.

He was in an alley when suddenly he was startled by a slight noise he could not identify. He froze back into the shadows. Soon he realized that the sounds came from a shed across the alley. He saw that the shed was the one in which old Repairman Chuan kept his tools.

Curiosity overcame Li Chi's fear. He inched his way around to the shed's door, which was slightly ajar. What he saw in the shed made him breathless with shock. Mrs. Chuan was there on a quilt with a man. What they were doing did not bother him— as an honest son of the soil he regarded such things as too natural to be disturbed about. It was the particular man with her that upset him. His beloved Mrs. Chuan was being embraced by the hated Meng.

Li Chi's first impulse was to leave immediately and put the abhorrent scene out of his mind. The artist in him made him pause and view the scene more objectively. Here was a chance to study light and shadow, line and form in rare combination.

Thus it was that Li Chi overheard what Meng said to Mrs. Chuan a few minutes later. "If you say anything about this, I'll deny it," he said, "and whom do you think Pu will believe, me or the village slut?" He got to his feet and stood over her. "But if you do open your mouth, I'll make you suffer until you curse the day you were born."

Mrs. Chuan said nothing, but in the moonlight Li Chi saw that her cheeks were wet with tears.

Li Chi melted into the shadows. To avoid Meng, he slipped into the village square and hid behind a tree. He sat there motionless, and thought.

He was glad that Mrs. Chuan had not chosen Meng for a lover, but he was sickened with rage that Meng was using his power to force himself on her. He understood that she did not dare complain; at first, he thought of reporting what he had seen and heard, but he dropped that idea at once. His small voice had no authority at all alongside Meng's, and speaking out might get her as well as himself in serious trouble. If only he could let everyone know what had happened without revealing where the information had come from.

He found himself looking across the square to the blank wall of the house in front of which Comrade Pu and the cadres sat at their two tables during the village political meetings. The wall was whitewashed and in the moonlight was dazzling white. It was a large virgin canvas crying for the kiss of color.

The crimson dye went smoothly into the hard, whitewashed mud. Li Chi painted in a daze. When he was through, he knew that the figures of Mrs. Chuan and Meng could be instantly recognized. Usually Mrs. Chuan's face was cheerful, but it showed suffering in Li Chi's drawing. Meng was made to look like a beast, and the fact that he was forcing Mrs. Chuan was clear. Finally, Li Chi had sketched in some of Mr. Chuan's tools so that everyone would know that the scene was the tool shed.

Li Chi carefully replaced the chair on which he had stood. He studied his work for a moment and then, contented, returned to his house.

Li Chi slept late the next morning and thus missed the first explosion his picture caused. When he got up, everyone was in the square. He wormed through the crowd and squatted in front. The villagers were being harangued by Meng. The grim-mouthed cadres sat at their tables.

Li Chi, however, looked first at his picture. He saw that an attempt to whitewash over it had been made; an oiliness in the dye, however, prevented the whitewash from sticking to it. Mud then had been smeared on the red, but it dropped off as soon as it dried. Li Chi grinned with delight.

Nevertheless, Li Chi grew a little uneasy when Meng's words began to sink in. Meng was hoarse and almost incoherent, but the threats he was making against the person who had painted that picture were as clear as they were dire. With a final shouted curse, he shook his fists at the crowd and sank down onto his chair.

Comrade Pu now stood up. His eyes were enormous behind his thick glasses, and seemed to flash with dark fire. Nevertheless, his high voice sounded more sad than angry. "There is great evil in this village," he said. "One among you is a diabolically clever counterrevolutionary. He has been well trained by his bourgeois masters. We will not rest until this enemy of the people has been found and exterminated—"

At this point, however, a murmuring came from the back of the crowd, and Pu seemed to realize that he had lost the attention of his audience. He interrupted himself to demand what had happened.

"Please, Comrade," a voice from the rear answered, "someone asked the fortune-teller who had painted that picture."

Li Chi's heart almost stopped beating.

"Indeed!" Pu said. "And what did that stupid old turtle say?"

"Ghosts!" the voice answered.

The crowd moaned. Mrs. Chuan screamed. Li Chi, however, sighed with relief and silently blessed his old friend. Comrade Pu lost his temper. He called his listeners superstitious idiots, and insisted that only an enemy spy could have painted the picture. Mrs. Chuan, however, broke up the meeting with her hysterics.

In the days that followed, the search for the painter of the picture went on ceaselessly. Methodically every adult in the village was interrogated. The children were left alone because no one could believe that a child could have either the skill or the evil intent necessary to be guilty of the drawing.

When it became clear that none of the villagers was guilty, the cadres leaned to the theory that an outsider had sneaked into the village that night, had done his dastardly deed, and then had cleverly managed to escape. The villagers scoffed at this. "How could a stranger come here at night and paint a picture that so perfectly caught the likenesses of Meng, Mrs. Chuan, *and* the interior of the handyman's shed?" they asked. "The fortune-teller was right," they added. *"Ghosts!"*

Life had never been so pleasant for Li Chi. Knowing that he was secretly responsible for much turmoil in the adult world filled him with delicious excitement. The only trouble was that now he dared not draw anything else, and he was afraid that any moment his jars of paint might be found.

Eventually, another aspect of the situation began to worry Li Chi. As the realization grew that the painter was not going to be found, the attention began to focus increasingly on Mrs. Chuan. Under her interrogation, she had broken down and confessed that she had been forced and threatened by Meng to do what the picture depicted.

This testimony had enraged the cadres. If they accepted it as true, they would have to admit that they had given a foul criminal the high honor of being made a hero of the land-reform movement and a Party member. According to their dogma,

23

however, the Party was infallible and a Party member was invariably the embodiment of all virtue. Thus, Mrs. Chuan had to be lying, and if she persisted in her falsehood she would be guilty of "casting aspersion on the nobility of a Party cadre," a crime for which the extreme penalty was often demanded.

Nevertheless, even the cadres had to admit that Mrs. Chuan's testimony sounded truthful—and that Meng's denials and bluster sounded false. Moreover, the cadres were aware that every one of the villagers believed Mrs. Chuan; they were not only completely sympathetic to her; they were also unmistakably hostile to Meng, despite the nobility that should have made him lovable.

A gulf began to widen between the villagers and the cadres. To protect their dogma—indeed, the very basis of their authority—the cadres could not let Mrs. Chuan's testimony go unrefuted and unpunished. Nevertheless, they also knew that the villagers were so angry that any attempt to bring charges against Mrs. Chuan might result in united opposition.

For the present, therefore, the issue was simply avoided. Pu had written in charcoal on the wall beside Li Chi's painting, "This is the work of a degenerate counterrevolutionary," but as time passed, people became used to the painting, and scarcely noticed it. Slowly, Li Chi perceived that this was what the cadres were waiting for. They would strike when the villagers had forgotten their anger. Mrs. Chuan would be convicted and sent away; the dogma would be vindicated and the Party's local record would be cleared. And all this would be accomplished before the villagers' anger could be rearoused.

Li Chi decided that it was time for the midnight ghost artist to strike again.

He waited a few more days until the moon would again give him good light to work by. Meanwhile, he planned every line of the sketch he would make on the bare whitewashed wall next to the one that carried his first picture. He also studied the propaganda posters and learned the characters for certain words.

24

Thus on the night he had been waiting for, he moved silently but quickly and efficiently. He retrieved his hidden dye and home-made brushes. He first wiped off the charcoal writing with which Pu had labeled the drawing of Meng and Mrs. Chuan. In its place, Li Chi wrote with his indelible dye the characters meaning, "This is the work of a people-loving injustice-hating ghost."

Now he moved to the new wall and began the new picture. Under his confident hands another drawing of Mrs. Chuan emerged. She was in the same shed and in a similarly compro-mising position. This time, however, she was laughing instead of crying. Her diminutive partner, his glasses askew and a look of desperation on his face, was attempting what everyone could see was limply impossible for him to achieve. Comrade Pu was shown as a failure in "overcoming the barrier of the masses." Li Chi stood back and studied the picture critically; he judged his work good.

But he still had more to do. After hiding his paint and brushes, he made his way to the one really good house in the village, the one now occupied by the cadres. He approached it from the rear. He climbed a tree, crawled out on a limb, and then dropped as silently as a leaf inside the garden wall. He flit-ted from shrub to tree as noiselessly as a moth. The shutters to Comrade Pu's room were ajar; they squeaked as Li Chi opened them more. The rhythm of Pu's snoring broke for a moment, then continued as before.

Li Chi jumped lightly over the windowsill and then stood mo-tionless in shadow. When the room seemed to accustom itself to his presence, he moved again. In one fluid motion, he snatched up Pu's glasses and trousers and then dived through the win-dow. He made himself wait until he was sure that Pu's snoring was calm and regular. Only then did he streak across the open space to the shelter of the shrubbery.

A few minutes later, Li Chi was in the alley behind Mr. Chuan's shed. Inside, he spread out the quilt. He tossed the glasses and trousers on it. Thereupon, his night's work was finished.

Back in his own house, excitement kept him awake. Moreover, at this time of year, the plowing had begun, and men went to the fields before dawn. Thus, although the sun rose and the women busied themselves with their stoves, still no commotion had been caused by his new painting. Li Chi got up and went out into the lane.

He saw now that people were hurrying toward the cadres' house. He joined them. In front of the house, they came upon a scene that utterly astonished Li Chi.

Comrade Pu, without his trousers and glasses, looked like a tiny fighting cock aroused to frenzied ferocity. He squawked like a cock as well. He staggered around wildly, striking out with his bony fists at every moving shadow. Sometimes he ran into a wall or tree, but this seemed only to add fuel to his rage. The lesser cadres pleaded with him, but when he heard their voices he charged in the direction of the sound. The village men were drifting back from the fields and they watched silently, in awe of the sheer magnificence of the little man's fury.

Suddenly, however, a piercing scream that froze the blood of every living creature in the village came from the direction of the square. Li Chi drew a deep breath. Mrs. Chuan, he knew, had seen the new picture.

Within minutes everyone had collected in the square, and all were standing in front of Li Chi's latest handiwork. The people stared at it silently, as though time were needed for the message to soak through their good solid peasant skulls.

Meanwhile Comrade Pu apparently sensed that something dramatic had happened; he followed the crowd, bumping into people, staggering and falling. In the square, he demanded in a loud voice to be told what was going on. What could anyone say? They made way for him, and he groped his way to the front. Here, he bumped into his table and then climbed to the top of it. "Every living person in this area," he announced, "will preoccupy himself solely with the task of discovering the where-abouts of my glasses and trousers. Until they are found, no other activity will be permitted."

After a moment's silence, someone from the crowd said, "If that picture is right, his pants and glasses should be in the tool shed." Automatically, the crowd turned and moved toward the alley.

In a matter of moments, the lost items were found. They were passed along quickly and finally handed up to Comrade Pu, still standing on the table. He put on his glasses first. He was about to put on his pants when something made him turn to see what the people were staring at. As he studied the picture, his pants slid unnoticed from his hands.

Someone in the crowd chuckled. Another did the same. In a moment the crowd was roaring with laughter. Some of the men rolled around on the ground, doubled up and helpless with mirth.

Eventually, however, Comrade Pu turned slowly to face the laughing crowd. His face was mottled black with anger. The intensity of it slowly smothered the laughter. "You will pay for this," he said when the crowd was quiet. "Every one of you will pay dearly for this indignity." He gave a signal to his deputies. "Meanwhile, we are going to struggle against one of you who has too long escaped the people's justice."

The deputies now forced their way roughly into the crowd. They seized Mrs. Chuan and dragged her to the front. She cried out, but they forced her to her knees.

For a moment, the people were silent. Then a current seemed to be switched on in the crowd. At first there was a murmur, but it swelled quickly into an angry roar. Then the mob moved forward.

Comrade Pu and his deputies did not hesitate. They turned and sprinted down the lane toward their house. The crowd followed; its anger mounted steadily, and when the cadres' house was reached the people were in a murderous rage.

Suddenly, however, the cadres reappeared. They were armed. Comrade Pu waved a big revolver over his head. "I have been given this weapon to liquidate enemies of the people," he shrieked. "I will not hesitate to shoot every one of you." Using both hands, he fired the revolver several times into the air.

The sound shocked the crowd. The anger turned quickly to panic. Within a minute, the mob had disintegrated; the lane was deserted except for the cadres.

Li Chi was more frightened than any of the others. He believed that the whole situation was entirely his fault. He felt that bloodshed now was unavoidable and that every drop shed would be on his hands. He knew well that although the villagers had panicked momentarily, the anger would soon overcome their fear. Undoubtedly they would swamp the cadres, but many villagers might be killed in the process.

He knew only one person who might help: the fortune-teller. Li Chi was breathless when he arrived at the hut. The old man sat on his bunk, nodding and muttering to himself. Li Chi threw himself on his knees. "Please, Fortune-teller," he said, "I need your help. You must listen to me."

The old man smiled. "I've been hoping you'd visit me," he said. "You must listen to *me*. It's about that recipe for the dye I gave you."

"Please, sir, *please*. There is no *time*," Li Chi pleaded.

"In my time, we were taught to respect our elders. Have the outsiders stolen all our manners too?" The old man held up an admonishing finger. "I must tell you that the recipe for that dye should include some of the leaves of the bush as well," he continued calmly. "The leaves are what make the dye absolutely permanent."

"There is trouble in the village. You must tell me what to do," Li Chi said.

"Get rid of your dye," the old man replied. "If you had used the leaves the dye would have been permanent, but it would have been deadly poison as well. Even what you have may be dangerous. Water will dilute it. Dump it immediately into the brook."

Li Chi cried out in anguish and frustration. "Something much more dangerous threatens," he said.

"My son, do not argue with an old man. Go at once and dispose of your dye," the fortune-teller said. "If you don't, I shall tell who painted those pictures—"

Li Chi was beaten. He did as he was told. Even so, he poured his precious dye into the brook slowly and reluctantly. As he returned to the village he saw that the brook water was running as red as blood. Then he remembered the fortune-teller's prophecy.

To Li Chi's dismay, the news that the brook was running red rearoused the villagers. They also remembered the prophecy that, on this occasion, they would drive the Communists from their land. They collected at the brookside to marvel at the miracle.

Li Chi was in despair, but he did not take into account the reaction of the cadres. When the Communists heard the villagers at the brook, they came out with their firearms, intending to disperse the mob before it became dangerous. When they saw the red waters, however, they also remembered the prophecy. For the moment, they forgot their indoctrination, and they panicked. They threw down their weapons, turned, and ran. They were pursued for many miles by the villagers, who dropped the chase only when they were sure that the cadres were so far away that they would not dare return.

Back in the village, however, the cooler heads reasoned that the Communists would not give up so easily and that many officials would soon return for a full-scale investigation. This seemed logical to Li Chi, and then he remembered that he had not destroyed the clay pots in which he had brewed the dye. Once again, he made his way up along the brook.

Just as he was breaking up the last of the pots, however, he was suddenly seized from behind and a voice said into his ear, "Finally, I've caught the little ghost who paints those pictures."

Li Chi cried out, and twisted in the arms that held him. He looked up into the angry face of Mrs. Chuan. "Please, I don't know what you mean," he said.

In answer, the woman grabbed his right hand and held it up in front of his face. He saw the red stains on his fingers. She also pointed to another stain on his shirt. "I saw that this morning in the square when Pu was looking for his glasses," she said. "I couldn't believe that you were the ghost, but I followed you to the old man's hut, and I heard what he said—"

"But I didn't mean you any harm," Li Chi pleaded. "What are you going to do?"

"Do!" she exclaimed. "You naughty boy! I'm going to give you a lesson I hope you'll never forget."

Li Chi was terrified. "Please, please!" he said. "I won't do it again."

"You certainly *will* do it again," she answered. She dropped his arm and shoved into his hand a pad of paper and a red crayon. "Look at me," she continued. "I'm not at all like you drew me on those walls. I'm not so fat *here,* and *here* I'm not as skinny as you showed me."

With that, in the shelter of the bushes, she proved to him that she was right. Li Chi had his first life class; it was a priceless lesson in anatomy. The sketch he now made of Mrs. Chuan satisfied her.

Mrs. Chuan and, apparently, the old fortune-teller as well, now knew that Li Chi was the "ghost" artist; thus, the secret soon leaked out. At first, the villagers were astonished, but by the time the new Communist officials arrived everyone was used to the idea; they considered that what had happened was no more than a childish prank.

This attitude was inevitably communicated to the new officials. They were accompanied by a strong detachment of "liberation" troops, and expected to find heavily armed, ferocious counterrevolutionists. This was the impression they had received from Comrades Pu and Meng and the other cadres.

The fact that the village was inhabited by the poorest of poor and peaceful peasants was only too obvious. On the other hand, it was also true that the serious crime of "detracting from the noble qualities of Party cadres" had been committed; the evidence was in two large but fading pictures in the village square. Nevertheless, who could be blamed for it? A poor woman whom the villagers had shown that they would fight hard to protect, and a skinny little kid! The Party cadres quickly decided to leave Mrs. Chuan alone—in these early days of the regime the Communists were not so sure of their power as they would be later—and the real question came down to whether or not Li Chi should or should not be punished.

Finally, the Party Secretary—the one who headed the new cadre group and the one who was responsible for preventing Comrades Pu and Meng from returning to the village—spoke his piece. "In all this talk about that kid Li Chi, you forget one important factor," he said. "The boy is geuninely talented. So far, he is the only 'son of toil' I've come across who has been anything but a clod. Forget about his little prank. If we punish him, we look foolish. If we drop the matter, we lose face and look weak. Our only alternative is to reward him—"

Thus it was that Li Chi found himself at the Art Institute in Peking. He was accompanied by such high recommendation that he was accepted without question even though he was much too young to enter the Institute formally.

Fortunately, one of the Institute's Party cadres took Li Chi in as a member of his own family. Li Chi was enrolled in a nearby grammar school. He now spent his full time doing what before he had delighted in doing whenever he had the time or the energy to spare from his labor on the farm. He studied hard at the standard school subjects, and he was given considerable instruction in art. He also was indoctrinated in Marxist ideology.

By the time he was sixteen, therefore, he was qualified in every respect, and he entered the Art Institute showing great promise.

CHAPTER II

First Love

Li Chi entered the Art Institute under the best possible circumstances, but almost immediately he began upon a course of action that sooner or later would lead him into trouble. At first, he was unaware that he was deviating from the prescribed path.

One day, however, he was disturbed by an item he read in the newspaper. What disturbed him most was the fact that he could not determine why the item disturbed him. He had read similar newspaper stories so often that he could have recited this one word for word without even seeing it. The story supposedly was by a young male machinist who described his reactions to a surprise visit to his factory by the local District Party Secretary.

"No! It could not be!" the machinist was credited with saying. "The Comrade District Party Secretary? The Comrade Party Secretary of *our* district? But then I saw the felicitous smile on my lathe partner's face. My heart began to pound wildly. 'The Comrade District Party Secretary?' I asked in an awed whisper. My partner was unable to reply; tears were

33

streaming down his face. He could only nod. Overcome with happiness, my partner and I embraced each other tightly. I felt the blood surging hot in my veins. My heart seemed to leap out of my breast. The Comrade District Party Secretary turned. He waved. I believed that he was waving only to me. I almost fainted with joy. I was weak with the agony of my exaltation. I found myself out in front of the factory staring in the direction of his car long after it had disappeared. My mind is still in a whirl even after all these days since the magnanimous visit of Comrade District Party Secretary. . . ."

Slowly, Li Chi perceived that, now for the first time, he understood the emotions and sensations described in all the newspaper stories like this one. The trouble was that, instead of having these feelings for his District Party Secretary, he felt them for Miss Fei. She was not even a Communist Youth League member, let alone a Party member and Secretary. She was only a girl. In short, Li Chi had fallen in love.

Love—romantic love—is abhorred by the Chinese Communists, and generally is depicted by them as a depravity of Westerners. Love is meant to be given only to socialism, the Party, and to Chairman Mao. Any other strong emotional attachment between people tends to be regarded as rejection of these three jealous authorities. Often, such rejection is treated as counterrevolutionism. At the least, it is apt to be looked upon as evidence of individualism, bourgeois or "rightist" thinking, as "failure to observe discipline," or as "failure to give one's heart to the Party."

These were the deadly sins toward which Li Chi was moving, but he was powerless to help himself. Merely thinking of the beautiful Miss Fei caused his heart to beat wildly. The sight of her made him weak with the agony of exaltation. And if she so much as glanced in his direction, he nearly fainted with joy.

What he especially liked about her was her shyness. On the rare occasions when someone in the group addressed her directly, she blushed and stammered in such visible distress that

Li Chi was almost overcome with protective feelings for her. The other group members seemed to respect Miss Fei's shyness, and they seldom spoke to her. Even Comrade Miss Keung, the scrawny Communist Youth League member who was the chairman of their discussion group, rarely even glanced through her thick-lensed glasses in Miss Fei's direction.

Thus, Li Chi was spared the pain of jealousy over his love, but because of his preoccupation with it he paid little attention to the political discussions. This irritated Comrade Miss Keung, who, despite protruding teeth and a bad lisp, had a viciously sharp tongue, which she used mercilessly on him. Miss Keung came from a proletarian background and, like many Chinese urban dwellers, made little effort to hide her contempt for peasants. Li Chi was aware that she blamed his vagueness, not on his feelings for Miss Fei, but on simple stupidity. He was willing to accept this, however, rather than suffer the agonizing embarrassment of having his love for Miss Fei held up for public ridicule.

At one meeting in late 1954, Miss Keung lectured the group at length on the problems of socialist construction. At the end, she questioned the group members to ensure that they had understood the lecture. Finally she asked Li Chi to list the eight barriers to the socialist transformation.

"The eight barriers to what?" he asked.

This was almost as bad as asking who was Mao Tse-tung. Li Chi saw Miss Keung's eyes widen enormously behind her thick glasses. He knew that he had gone too far and that he was in for serious trouble.

At that moment, however, the classroom door opened and Comrade Hsi entered. He was in his middle twenties, the Party member who headed the Institute's Youth League organization. At infrequent intervals he inspected the various discussion-group meetings. His arrival brought about a miraculous change in Miss Keung. She blushed and fluttered. Although no one could say that she had suddenly become pretty, one did notice for the first time that she might be female. "Oh, Comrade Hsi," she said, "you've come at last to share with us your vast political wisdom."

"Not at all," the inspector said. "I'll just sit here quietly and listen to you young people. Go on with your meeting." He sat down by Miss Fei, but he smiled at Miss Keung.

When Miss Keung recovered her composure, she explained what was being discussed at the meeting. "Unfortunately," she said then, "our Mr. Li Chi seems totally unfamiliar with the eight barriers to socialist transformation."

To Li Chi's surprise, Inspector Hsi interrupted Miss Keung. "Naturally Mr. Li Chi would not know the barriers," he said. "Mr. Li Chi comes from a peasant worker background. He surmounted the barriers automatically. Those barriers exist only for the bourgeoisie. . . ."

Li Chi realized that fate had interceded in his behalf, but he knew that he would not have another chance. Nevertheless, instead of forgetting Miss Fei as he should have done, he made an effort to see even more of her. He managed to get himself transferred to a drawing class she was in. The class work was more advanced than he was trained to do, but he promised to work hard to catch up. He hoped that he could impress Miss Fei with his industry and talent.

On the third day of this class, the students were required to submit a still-life drawing of a pine branch and cone. Li Chi concentrated his whole attention on the assignment, and did his very best work. When the drawings were exhibited in front of the class, however, he saw that Miss Fei's was far superior to all the others. His own was almost at the bottom. In fact, only Comrade Miss Keung's was worse. Her paper showed that she had started the drawing and had made a mess of it. She then had drawn a large "X" across the paper and had written: "This is a stupid assignment. How does it aid socialist construction?"

To Li Chi's amazement, however, the teacher gave Miss Keung's paper the highest possible mark. His own paper was given the same grade. The others received lower marks, but Miss Fei's paper was graded as a failure. Moreover, the teacher criticized her unmercifully for showing "decadent bourgeois influences" in her work.

Miss Fei took the teacher's abuse with meekly bowed head. Li Chi suffered badly in her behalf; he wanted desperately to comfort her. At the same time, he thought that, secretly at least, she must hate him for getting the grade that only she deserved. The fact that she was the victim of injustice and that he could do nothing to help her was more than he could bear.

After the class, he hurried away so that she would be spared having to see him. The next morning, however, the Institute's students and faculty were called out to march all morning through Peking in a "spontaneous" demonstration against a speech made in the UN by the American representative. Li Chi found himself near Miss Fei in the crowd. An irresistible impulse made him push his way to her side. "Please," he said, "I could not stand to see your beautiful drawing criticized. It was so unfair. Yours was the best in the class."

At first she was startled, but after a moment her face softened, and she almost smiled at him. Then, however, he saw her become afraid. "Protest America's warmongering imperialist policies!" she shouted, and her eyes besought him to go away.

Li Chi felt that he had crossed a tremendous barrier; he had achieved direct communication with his love, and he was not going to abandon the position without a struggle.

"I am not going to stand for it," he said to her. "I am going to insist that you get the grade I got and that I get the one given to you." Thereupon, he looked around and said loudly, "Discredit the slanderous lies of gangster Eisenhower!"

"Oppose the hypocritical peace moves of the imperialist stooges," she said to the sky, and then softly to him: "Please. You'll only make more trouble. Don't you understand? I come from a bourgeois background. So does the teacher. He doesn't dare give me good grades."

In the days that followed, Li Chi learned that grades were given, not for the quality of the work done, but on the basis of the student's class background. According to the dogma, all virtue was found exclusively in the working classes and all evil in the bourgeoisie. This supposed truism would be contradicted if Miss Fei, who was from "an unacceptable class element," were given a higher grade than Comrade Miss Keung, who was "progressive." Miss Fei maintained her position at the Institute by sheer competence, but her talent was never given official recognition. Comrade Miss Keung had been rewarded with admission to the Institute because she had served the authorities faithfully and because her class background was "pure."

Li Chi quickly realized that any attempt to change the circumstances would only make them worse for his love. Nevertheless, now that he had established contact with her he could not give it up. He saw her whenever he could. Despite her hesitation and worries, she had been desperately lonely, and she welcomed his company. He made her feel that he was on her side, and he assured her that because his own background was pure, the authorities would consider that he would be having a good progressive influence on her. He did not say that the authorities might equally take the opposite view of their relationship, that is, that she was having a contaminating influence on him.

The bashful romance between Li Chi and Miss Fei bloomed through the chill Peking winter of late 1954 and early 1955. The happy couple almost came to believe that they had nothing to worry about. Certainly neither of them saw anything ominous in the fact that Comrade Inspector Hsi took to dropping in on their discussion-group meetings at least once a week and sometimes oftener. The only noticeable effect of this was that Comrade Miss Keung obviously was flattered, and she fluttered and lisped in an actually feminine manner.

One afternoon, however, as a meeting was breaking up, Comrade Hsi spoke to Miss Fei. With a lover's sensitivity, Li Chi perceived in an intuitive flash that Comrade Hsi also was in love with the beautiful Miss Fei and that he had been coming to the meetings to see her and not to admire Comrade Miss Keung's progressive efficiency. Li Chi heard a sibilant indrawn breath behind him. He turned and saw Miss Keung. He saw that she also had had an intuitive flash and that she now understood the real reason for the inspector's visits. A look of sheer hatred twisted her face. Li Chi knew with sickening despair that Miss Fei had earned the deadly hatred of a powerful enemy.

Miss Keung's revenge was not long in coming. At this time the authorities were introducing another suppression campaign. It became known as the "elimination of counterrevolutionaries." Like the "thought reform movement" of three years before, it was aimed at intellectuals, and was meant to terrorize them into subservience.

The campaign had been caused by a famous writer named Hu Feng. He was an old-time Party member, but he believed that the only worthwhile creativity resulted from the self-expression of an artist, who therefore should have the freedom to develop his individuality. To the Party politicians this meant advocating the criminal offense of individualism. The only function of the artist, they said, was to follow Party directions in making his contribution to socialist construction. Hu Feng and a number of like-minded associates joined together to make their combined voices sound louder. Nothing ever aroused the Communist leaders more than *united* opposition, no matter how small, to their policies. They moved at once. Hu Feng and his followers disappeared. Next, an almost hysterical search was made throughout the country to expose thoughts similar to those of Hu Feng. Only intellectuals were likely to have such thoughts, and the campaign was directed mainly at them. Intellectuals associated with the arts were under the greatest suspicion. Thus the students and faculty at the Art Institute were required to participate in the campaign to the fullest extent.

The process required each individual to write a lengthy autobiography in which the social and political opinions he had held throughout his life were revealed. Thereupon, the autobiography was discussed by his fellow group members, who searched it for falsehood and omissions. In practice, most of the autobiographies were passed without comment. A person with Li Chi's background, for example, had nothing to fear because he was assumed to have the right thoughts automatically. The custom was, however, for the cadres to single out one or two "heavy points" in most discussion groups. These unfortunates were to be "struggled against." On the threat of being "struggled against" themselves, the other group members were made to turn upon and denounce the "heavy points." The victims were harangued, cursed, reviled, spat upon, and even beaten. They were accused of innumerable crimes and pressed to confess. The ordeal went on until the victims were broken into confessing what the cadres had decided in advance would be appropriate. Thereupon, the masses decreed a punishment, invariably harsh, which the cadres also had decided upon in advance.

Perhaps the most effective aspect of this process was that the victims were invariably innocent of the crimes for which they were convicted and punished; moreover, everyone in the group knew that the victims were innocent. Thus the suffering of the victims was a purely abstract lesson in what the other group members could expect if unacceptable thinking should be discovered in them.

In Li Chi's group, Miss Fei was made the "heavy point."

Fortunately, Li Chi himself was not expected to denounce and revile her. It was the other students who came from bourgeois backgrounds who had to prove their progressiveness and loyalty to the regime by attacking her. Li Chi suffered as badly as she did under the attack. After the third day of her ordeal, he saw that she was beginning to break. He was terrified now that she might commit suicide; a high percentage of the victims in this campaign were taking their own lives. Li Chi would gladly have given his life to save her. She was kept under guard, however, from the time she left the girls' dormitory until she returned there, and Li Chi therefore could not even speak to her.

Although Miss Fei's position seemed hopeless, one aspect of it kept recurring to Li Chi. Comrade Miss Keung obviously had been responsible for having Miss Fei made a heavy point, but such a decision usually was made at a much higher level. In fact, someone like Inspector Hsi would have been the logical person to do it, and yet Li Chi was sure that the man loved Miss Fei. This meant that Miss Keung, in a fit of jealous rage, must have exceeded her authority and had somehow forced her superiors to accept her decision. Li Chi knew that, in order to maintain the appearance of unity, the authorities might accept Miss Keung's decision now, but punish her for her effrontery later. Unfortunately, this was not much help to poor Miss Fei. Nevertheless, Li Chi decided that somehow he must manage to see Miss Fei and discuss the situation with her.

After the struggle meeting that day, Li Chi followed her as she returned to the dormitory with her guards. The guards left her at the door. Just as Li Chi was trying to think what he could do next, he saw her slip out of the door and hurry toward the street, where she quickly lost herself in the crowd.

Li Chi ran after her, but he was carrying an armload of drawing materials and could not move through the crowd as quickly. To Li Chi's surprise, Miss Fei led him through the city streets to the Lama Temple, which in honor of the Dalai Lama's visit from Tibet had been refurbished. Li Chi was not religious himself, but he understood that the girl in her hour of great trouble might seek some kind of spiritual consolation. From outside, he watched, deeply touched, while Miss Fei stood motionless, her head bowed, and for the moment seemingly at peace.

Suddenly, however, Li Chi noticed that another man was watching Miss Fei. He recognized the type immediately; a middle-aged, long-time Party member who had been made arrogant and officious by his authority. Li Chi saw that the man disapproved of the fact that Miss Fei was praying. Finally, the man took out a pen and notebook and walked toward the girl.

41

Li Chi was panic-stricken. If an outside complaint of backwardness and "bourgeois superstition" were lodged against Miss Fei now, the results could only be catastrophic for her. He found that he had stepped forward and had put a hand on the man's arm. "Excuse me, Comrade," he said. "Could we ask your advice?"

"What do you want?" the man asked. He frowned with impatience.

"We are from the Art Institute," Li Chi said, indicating the girl. "Miss Fei is trying to decide how this temple should be depicted."

"Why don't you illustrate our country's progress in the glorious task of socialist construction instead of this monument to feudalistic superstition?" the man said.

"Miss Fei believes that, right now, the Party policy on religious freedom among the minorities needs to be illustrated." Li Chi spoke much more confidently than he felt, and he saw the man blink. "Miss Fei fears that misunderstanding might arise about the situation in the Tibet region. Our glorious military forces have made a great sacrifice to go into Tibet to aid socialist construction there, but some people might get the erroneous impression that the Tibetans have resisted the Party's wise policies. Miss Fei wants me to help her illustrate unforgettably how our regime has protected these religious treasures that mean so much to the Tibetan people. I thought you might give us some advice."

To Li Chi's relief, something that resembled grudging approval appeared on the man's face. At the mention of her name, Miss Fei had turned, and now she approached hesitantly. The man became aware of her beauty, and his expression showed even more approval. "I don't know anything about art," he began.

"Oh, sir, you are too modest. We would have only the greatest respect for your judgment," Li Chi said. He had broken out into a cold sweat.

"What you should do is show those Tibetan turtles that we spent a lot of the people's money on this damn temple," the man said.

Li Chi nodded. "I see your point, sir," Li Chi said. He then turned to Miss Fei and took her arm. "Draw as you never did before," he whispered to her. "It's your one chance."

He saw that she understood. As she took paper and colored pencils from him, he saw also that hope and gratitude had rekindled her vitality.

When Li Chi could control the trembling of his hands, he also began to draw, and he did it as he had never done it before. He drew Miss Fei, but he put her in a colorful Tibetan costume. He showed her in the sumptuous interior of the temple lit by the late-afternoon sun. He expressed in his work all the emotion he felt for the girl, and he knew that this work was the best he had ever done. Miss Fei's was even better. Moreover, Li Chi saw that the man also was impressed. "I may be only the District Party Secretary," he said, "but I know good art when I see it." He took paper and a pen from Li Chi. "I want you to send those drawings to the editor of the paper. Send them with this note from me—"

Li Chi was in a daze. "Comrade District Party Secretary!" he exclaimed. "Please, Comrade, perhaps you could write another note to Comrade Hsi who is head of the Youth League organization at our Institute."

The man showed impatience, but he took the pad again. "Comrade Hsi," he wrote, "Congratulations on your two talented students Miss Fei and Mr. Li Chi. They have shown commendable progressiveness in implementing Party policy."

As soon as Li Chi and Miss Fei were alone, Li Chi sat down on the steps of a public building to write a newspaper story to go with the two pictures. He did not have to think what to say; he knew the words by heart. "No! It could not be!" he wrote. "The District Party Secretary? The Party Secretary of *our* district? But then I saw the felicitous smile and the tears of joy streaming down my partner's face. We embraced each other tightly. . . ."

Apparently, Li Chi had appraised the situation at the Art Institute correctly. The note about Miss Fei's progressiveness from the District Party Secretary enabled Comrade Hsi to intercede for her. A week later, Miss Keung vanished; the rumor was that she had been made the propaganda secretary for a small agricultural cooperative in the Northwest wilderness.

Li Chi, together with Miss Fei, had their first taste of publicity when their pictures and Li Chi's little story appeared in the paper. Unfortunately, however, Miss Fei could not be given a complete reprieve. The struggle against her had gone too far. She was made to do two weeks of manual labor on the Institute's grounds and then was dismissed from the school. Li Chi was heartbroken when she was gone, and he wrote to her formal little letters that only partially disguised the tender feelings he had for her. She answered similarly, but within two months she married an engineer and moved to a district in the South.

Li Chi suffered badly for several months. He worked hard to make himself forget. He paid little attention to political affairs, but he did not get into trouble again until two years later, in early 1957.

CHAPTER III

Weeds and Flowers

The struggle against Miss Fei conditioned Li Chi's attitude toward the authorities; he saw them now as malicious and hostile. In this he was little different from his Anhwei peasant forebears who, with good reason, had almost always regarded those who held political power as the natural enemy.

By 1957, however, Li Chi's attitude toward the "natural enemy" had undergone another important change. He no longer looked upon them as individuals whose personal malevolence he needed to circumvent. He had learned that those who had power over his destiny were what they were because of their ideology rather than from any natural flaws of character. In other words, they were good or evil to the extent that Communism was good or evil; thus, if one understood Communism one could predict (and therefore be forewarned about) much of the Communists' behavior.

It is important to appreciate that Li Chi was—is—apolitical to that special degree of which only the Chinese seem capable. He is concerned primarily with survival, not ideology. Put into any political order, he would seek instinctively the flaws, contradictions, and loopholes in the political structure; these would be the weaknesses of the regime that he could use against the authorities for his own benefit. Perhaps he has an inbred cynicism that makes him incapable of expecting good from any social order. In any case, his idea of a "good" ideology is one with weaknesses that he is able to exploit.

The primary ideological weakness of the Chinese Communists is their preoccupation with absolutes. In effect, by refuting only one aspect of the dogma, the infallibility of the entire ideology is threatened and the whole basis on which the Communists justify their seizure of political power is undermined. For this reason, much of the energy of the Communist officials, particularly on the lower levels, is spent in maintaining illusions, in sustaining the official pretense that things are what the dogma says they should be.

The aspect of this weakness that Li Chi found most useful was the familiar dogma about the unalterable characteristics of each class group. At the Art Institute, the majority of the students and almost all the teachers had come from the bourgeoisie. The dogma decreed, however, that anyone with this background was insensitive, uncreative, degenerate, and stupid. Conversely, the majority of "working-class elements" among the students had been enrolled for political reasons rather than for talent, but the dogma said that they alone would possess the real creativity, energy, and intelligence. They were, of course, the worst students; therefore the pretenses necessary to protect the dogma from this truth were elaborate indeed.

Li Chi, however, was the Institute's one living example that seemed to uphold the dogma. His talent was genuine, he was an exceptional student, and his working-class background was ideal. He represented the group for whose benefit the Communists justified their authority. Hence, it was most important to them that Li Chi would acknowledge that he was benefited by them and that he recognized the need for their leadership. If he would do this, they would reward him greatly; above all, they would allow him to enter the ranks of the elite by becoming a Party member himself.

Nevertheless, Li Chi resisted this honor. He perceived that Party membership would bring him material benefits and economic security but that it would also mean being subjected to an iron discipline that would quickly stamp out his individuality. Moreover, once in the Party, he too would become preoccupied with the need to justify the overweening privileges.

It would be better for him, he decided, to remain always in the position of being wooed by the authorities. The security of this position might not be great, but it should provide him with as much material advantage as he wanted and above all allow him the independence he needed in order to become a really competent artist.

Not long after Miss Fei left the Institute, therefore, Li Chi began deliberately to resist the Party's claim on him. Slowly the pressure on him was increased. "Under the old regime, you were scum, and you would have amounted to nothing," he was told repeatedly, "but in the new society you are given respect, a free education, economic security, and the opportunity to achieve fame and fortune. These gifts come to you from the glorious Communist Party under the inspired leadership of our beloved Chairman Mao. Aren't you glad to have the gifts? Aren't you grateful for them?"

"No," Li Chi would reply. "You Communists aren't giving me anything. I am being made an artist, not for my benefit, but solely so that my talent can be exploited for your advantage. I am really only a peasant. I did not ask to be made into an artist, and I don't want to be one. I'll be content only when I am allowed to be a peasant again."

This infuriated the Institute's authorities, but they would not send him back to the fields. There were already too many farm laborers, but there was a shortage of genuine "people's artists" who could uphold the myths about "proletarian culture." The authorities' only recourse was to offer Li Chi even more inducements.

Nevertheless, what Li Chi was doing was extremely dangerous. Eventually, the authorities realized that he was taking advantage of them. This meant facing the fact that his motives and attitudes were the opposite of what the dogma decreed they should be in a person like him. Publicly, they might never destroy the illusion that he was a fragrant flower of the socialist society, but privately they would work toward his total destruction. Li Chi therefore considered the possibility of a strategic retreat.

On the other hand, the idea occurred to him that aggression rather than surrender might be beneficial. With this in mind, he began for the first time to think in terms of intrigue and to make a careful study of the Institute's authorities.

As far as Li Chi was concerned, the "authorities" were the Party Secretary and the man's deputy who were in charge of the department in which Li Chi was enrolled. They were Comrades Cheng and Tan respectively. Over these cadres was the all-powerful Party Secretary for the whole Institute, but except for occasional inspection visits he was never seen.

Of the two cadres, Li Chi considered the deputy Tan the most dangerous. Previously the closest Tan had been to "art" had been the Communist posters that, when he was a city urchin in the days of the old regime, Party members had paid him to paste on walls at night. Tan was not merely indifferent to art; he openly detested it. Perhaps he sensed that it had some kind of power—a power that he could not understand and that he therefore feared and hated. He sneered at the efforts of the art students, and he was often obstructionist when he could get away with it without incurring the displeasure of his own superiors. Although he was the lesser in rank, he was the more intelligent. Furthermore, it was suspected that he had a special role—probably as an informer for the Party—so that his authority may have equaled Cheng's.

Party Secretary Cheng was a type Li Chi recognized and understood: a stolid, unimaginative peasant who had been coarsened by poverty, war, and Communist "discipline." He was barely literate, but he lived and breathed "revolution." He approved of "art" as long as it depicted what he called "socialist action." He particularly liked pictures of Party martyrs suffering unspeakable tortures from Nationalist police or of battle scenes in which the comrades were shown dispatching their class enemies in gruesomely ingenious ways.

In effect, Tan and Cheng were responsible for the education of the art students. It is not surprising that they were hated and feared by the students and faculty alike.

At this time, in the spring of 1957, the major issue in Communist China—and the one that, through almost daily discussion-group meetings, brought Li Chi into frequent contact with cadres Cheng and Tan—concerned Mao's famous speech "On the Correct Handling of Contradictions Amongst the People." By this time, a number of the regime's shortcomings could no longer be hidden from the rest of the world, let alone from the mainland Chinese people. To explain them, the authorities blamed lower-echelon government cadres whose excessive zeal and failure to educate the masses properly had sometimes led to "contradictions between the people and the government. These contradictions led to confusion and misunderstandings that, in turn, brought on instances of injustice, inefficiency, and stagnation. To solve the problem, the "working style" of the government cadres needed to be improved. The order was that the cadres were to "learn from the masses," who would be encouraged to air their personal grievances, point out mistakes made by the cadres, search for weaknesses in Party policy, and criticize any deficiencies in the new society. The expectation was that new ideas, like hundreds of blossoms, would bloom. The good ideas would be fragrant flowers; the bad ideas would be poisonous weeds.

Thus did Mao Tse-tung introduce the astonishing, short-lived

"Hundred Flowers" period. The campaign began to get out of hand almost from the moment the people had been persuaded to believe that their criticism was expected and that they would not be punished for giving it. In the universities, the science students usually were the ones who "bloomed," that is, offered their criticism, most violently and bitterly. This was because the pseudoscience of Communism invariably took precedence over, and often contradicted, the real science they studied

Nevertheless, the fine-arts students and the faculty members at the Art Institute were bitter in their complaints against the hated Cheng and Tan. Li Chi saw that the two cadres were confused and frightened by the criticism; they seemed to feel that they had been abandoned by the authorities and left alone to face the wrath of the masses. Their fear made the "masses" even bolder, and the students' "blossoming" became increasingly sharp.

Li Chi listened carefully to the criticism. To him, the complaints sounded like whining petulance. At the most, they could temporarily undermine the Communists' justification for holding power, but they would never persuade the Communists to give up the power. Time and again, the authorities had demonstrated their ability to maintain the most elaborate pretenses against encroaching fact and truth. What evidence was there that the Communist leaders had suddenly become obsessed with objective reality?

None, as far as Li Chi could see. He therefore avoided "blossoming" as long as he could, while he studied the reactions of Cheng and Tan. He noticed that Cheng's eyes gleamed with satisfaction whenever the criticism was directed at Tan. Similarly, he saw that Tan's poker-faced imperviousness seemed to crack into something resembling human gloating whenever the criticism was directed at Cheng. Whenever Cheng spoke, Li Chi noticed that the man watched and chose his words with great care, but at the same time was frustrated and infuriated by the necessity for doing so. On the other hand, whenever Cheng exercised his superior authority, Tan was unable to keep an angry sneer from his face.

Li Chi now began to prepare a speech for his own "blooming." He wrote it carefully and memorized it until he was sure that his delivery would be letter perfect. At the same time, he made friends with the matronly woman clerk * in the office of the Party Secretary for the entire Institute. On occasion, this top cadre would quietly and unexpectedly enter one of the discussion-group meetings, sit in the back, and observe the proceedings. Li Chi refrained from blossoming until the day he learned from the clerk that his group meeting could expect a visit from the top Party Secretary.

"I am in complete agreement with the Party's policy of inviting constructive criticism in order that the work of the cadres can be improved," Li Chi began his blossoming. He was worried that the Institute's Party Secretary might not appear, and he watched the door anxiously. "I have thought long and hard about what criticism, coming from me, would help the most. From the first, I realized that my criticism would be invalid and worthless unless it was based on my personal experience. Soon, in my thinking, I was forced to face the fact that my experience was severely limited. Finally I reached the humble conclusion that I am not competent to offer the Party criticism." At this, a murmur of disapproval came from the students, and Comrade Cheng raised his eyebrows in surprise. "Nevertheless," Li Chi went on, "I am sure that the cadres are not perfect. Chairman Mao has said so. I believe that the Party *should* be criticized but the criticism must be expert and informed, not the mere bicker-

* A female assistant to this woman escaped to Hong Kong a few months later. She is one of those who believe strongly that Li Chi really exists. She is an important source—but not the only one— of information about Li Chi's early life. She claims that she had acquired the information from her familiarity with the Institute's biographical files of the students.

ing of amateurs. Consider, for example, that the work of us art students is criticized by both amateurs and experts, but which opinion do we ourselves value and act upon? The expert opinion, of course. Really constructive criticism can come only from our fellow artists who know our problems and difficulties, who understand what we try to achieve and can perceive where we have succeeded or failed. The same situation must exist with the Party cadres. They have studied at the same revolutionary school; they have shared revolutionary experience; and only they can understand fully the problems of working with the unenlightened masses, of leading those who, perhaps, do not want to be led, of teaching those who may be unwilling to learn. Thus, only the cadres, and the cadres alone, can offer each other criticism that is of value."

At this point, to Li Chi's relief, the Party Secretary entered silently and, unobserved by the audience, took a seat at the back. Li Chi's listeners were completely attentive. Some of the students seemed surprised or baffled by his unusual approach to blossoming. Others were showing disgust because Li Chi seemed to be toadying to the Party authorities. Comrade Tan's face was expressionless, but Cheng seemed pleased. Li Chi now turned suddenly to Cheng and addressed him directly. "Comrade Party Secretary," he said, "I would ask *you* to give us the benefit of your criticism of the Party in general and of Comrade Tan in particular. Does Comrade Tan as your subordinate perform his duties satisfactorily? Can you suggest ways in which his working style could be improved?"

Cheng obviously was too astonished to speak for a moment. "Of course Comrade Tan does an excellent job," he said, when he had regained his composure, "on the whole. I could suggest that he might make himself available more often to assist me. Half the time he is off somewhere. He is supposed to be my assistant. And that exhibition last week. Anyone would assume that for a hundred pictures the large hall would be used. Comrade Tan's decision, made behind my back, to use the small exhibition room was a mistake. No wonder the affair was a failure."

"It wasn't the hall," Comrade Tan said, jumping up. "It was the pictures you always choose. Why should anyone want to look at a hundred pictures of corpses and blood? And if you want my candid opinion, your decision to include three ex-generals on the judging committee ought to be criticized severely."

"I will defend that decision staunchly," Comrade Cheng said loudly. "Those comrades are honored heroes of the liberation. As for your criticism of my choice of pictures, I am astonished. What you are really criticizing is our great liberation movement that was made under the inspired leadership of our commander and comrade Chairman Mao Tse-tung. Are you suggesting that Comrade Mao's words, 'A revolution is not a tea party,' should be forgotten? Are you suggesting—"

"I am suggesting," Tan interrupted, "that you should write a self-criticism report to the Institute's Party Secretary confessing your incompetence and submitting your resignation."

"And I'm warning *you*," Cheng said through clenched teeth, "that a report on your insubordination, rightist individualism and bourgeois indiscipline will be sent immediately to the Secretary—"

At this moment, the Party Secretary at the back of the room rose slowly. He was thin-lipped, but he spoke calmly. "Neither report will be necessary, Comrades," he said, "but we will discuss the matter in my office at once."

Two days later, cadres Cheng and Tan disappeared. Their replacements were new to the Institute. They quickly perceived in Li Chi the ideal student, the living proof of the superiority of socialist culture. If only he could be persuaded to cooperate more with the Party . . . Surely all he needed was a bit more encouragement, an added inducement or two.

Meanwhile Li Chi pretended to be as surprised as everyone else at the sudden departure of the two hated cadres. Nevertheless, if he was guilty of some small feeling of self-satisfaction, who can blame him? Not many had been able to "blossom" and to eradicate a couple of weeds at the same time.

CHAPTER IV

The Peasants' Mural

The period of the "Hundred Flowers" lasted through May and June, 1957. As Li Chi had surmised, the authorities would not accept the type of criticism they received. Even worse was the fact that almost universal hatred of the Communists was unmistakably revealed in the criticism. According to the dogma, however, the people should love the Communists, not hate them. In characteristic fashion, therefore, the Communists set about suppressing the unacceptable truth

The first step was to suspend any further freedom of speech and to clamp down on even the mildest criticism of the regime. Next, all evidence that the people had ever expressed antagonism to the regime was methodically destroyed. Finally, the fact that the antagonism had ever existed was officially denied. Anyone who said otherwise was a rightist or a counterrevolutionary, and one death was too good for him.

The anti-rightist campaign introduced the suppression that began in June of 1957 and lasted into early 1958. The customary terror tactics of "struggle" were used, but this time they were applied so rigorously that within a few months the entire population groveled. Apathetic and listless, the people became like domesticated animals who did only what they were ordered to do.

When every vestige of antagonism to the regime had been stamped out, the Hundred Flowers campaign was reinstated. Now, however, everyone knew that only the most fulsome praise, disguised as criticism, was acceptable. At the Art Institute, typical blooming was, "I criticize the Communist cadres for being overgenerous and lenient. We students are given too much food, too many comforts, and too many educational opportunities." At the same time, the masses were made to produce millions of posters on such themes. These tactics fooled no one on the mainland, but were useful in the regime's propaganda abroad.

Once the pretense had been established that the masses had criticized the regime freely and spontaneously, they next were made to demonstrate that there had been no animosity in their criticism. Thus the campaign now inaugurated by the government as a "spontaneous mass movement" was called "Give Your Heart to the Party." Each person was made to vie with his fellow discussion-group members in the mawkishness with which he proclaimed his love for the Party and the cadres. Within only a week or so, however, the emphasis shifted to a new overlapping campaign called the "Double Anti" (anti-bourgeois and anti-individualism). The idea was that, having given his heart to the Party, a person now desired only to become "a willing tool of the Party." To this end, he "spontaneously" strove to eliminate vestiges of bourgeois thinking, which, to the students, meant avoiding the concept of "learning for the sake of learning"; instead, a student was to learn only that which the Party found useful for him to learn. "Individualism" meant the effrontery of thinking for oneself or of having opinions of one's own. All major decisions were to be arrived at only through the consensus reached in one's discussion group, directed by the Party's representative.

This was the point at which Li Chi understood the extent of the regime's antagonism to the type of creativity without which he now was incapable of living. Until now, his background had given him an advantage, and because he had been adequately cooperative his position was secure. Before long, however, his "individualism" would be found out, and then nothing would stay the hostility of the authorities toward him. For the first time Li Chi endured the distress of acute insecurity.

As a result of this insecurity, his desire to return to his own type of people, and to the life he understood, became overpowering. Even the physical aspects of his life at the Institute began to gall him. Previously, for example, he had been able to make little more than a token attendance at his group-discussion meetings, and even then he usually slept through them. Now, however, he dared not miss one, or miss anything that went on in them. Moreover, for weeks at a time, the meetings, sometimes several hours long, would be held every day; they cut drastically into the time and energy he could devote to painting. Perhaps just as bad was the fact that during each of these campaigns, the masses had been made to turn out posters every day. The result was that paper of every kind and all the inks and paints were used up so rapidly that the country has suffered desperate shortages ever since. To Li Chi this monumental waste churned his very soul. In Peking he was only one among thousands competing for the meager supplies of paper, ink, and paints. He thought that in the country he would have less competition for the locally available paper and, possibly, could make his own ink or vegetable colors. Thus, Li Chi determined to leave Peking, even if to do so required desperate action.

At this time, surprisingly, he had little chance of succeeding. The government made university education virtually free, but in return a student was expected to accept without demur the post assigned to him by the authorities. Positions away from the urban centers in small towns or rural districts were considered by the authorities and by most of the students to be the least desirable. The assignments were made, not on the basis of a student's capability, but on his class background. Most of the arts students were city-bred ex-bourgeoisie who loathed everything rural and lived in terror of being sent into the countryside; the authorities invariably sent them to the farthest possible rural districts. The most desirable posting was an assignment at the Institute as an instructor. Such jobs always were given to students who had a peasant or worker background and who might have been willing to go into the far districts. Within his group of fellow students, Li Chi not only had the most desirable class background; he also had the most talent. This assured him of the assignment the authorities considered the best. He had been told unofficially, in fact, that he would be kept on at the Institute after graduating.

Before the anti-rightist campaign, a graduating student could protest his government-assigned job; if he argued persuasively enough and was able to hold out long enough, he sometimes won his point, or at least a compromise of some kind. Since the "Give Your Heart to the Party" and the Double-Anti campaigns, however, this was impossible; even to suggest that one was less than ecstatic at the authorities' decision concerning the job assignment was to call down charges of "individualism" and to ensure that the assigned job would be insisted upon adamantly.

In late May, 1958, the emphasis in the Double-Anti campaign was shifted to the concept of "red and expert," which was to preoccupy the Communists for the next two years. Henceforth, all education, apprenticeship, or job training was to be accompanied by an equal amount of training in "political awareness" or "redness." The result would be, according to theory, that as each person became more proficient in his profession he would simultaneously become more conscious of his political responsibility, which meant "being submissive to the will of the Party and active in carrying out the Party's will." The opposite was also held to be true: that is, as a person became more "red" he automatically would become more expert in his profession; this was held to be logical on the basis that an individual's only function or purpose was to be useful to the Party so that one's *willingness* to be useful and *ability* to be useful finally would blend into the indistinguishable concept of "red and expert."

During the period when Li Chi's political group were discussing this topic, he was asked to join a delegation of other experts of various kinds to visit a large collective farm near Peking. This was the type of agricultural unit that, within six months, would become a "production brigade" of an agricultural commune.

Li Chi was included among the delegates because the peasants had painted a huge mural on the wall of the barn that was used as the collective's mess and assembly hall; as a "red" and an expert, Li Chi was meant to express official approbation for this example of the "people's art." Li Chi had no difficulty in finding praise for the local "artists." He was so happy to be among his own kind of people again that he would not have dreamed of saying anything unpleasant. Moreover, he realized immediately that the peasants were deeply disturbed. They were being subjected to increasingly intense propaganda, and they knew that the authorities were preparing to make even greater demands upon them. Li Chi longed to be living once again among the peasants, so that he could use his greater knowledge of the Communists in order to help and protect his own people.

On the trip back from the collective, he found that his thoughts turned increasingly to the mural itself. He had learned that the peasants had not painted it spontaneously; the task had been imposed upon them by the collective's Party Secretary. The painting pictured the produce cultivated on the farm. The products were depicted, however, in fantastic size. The wheat, for example, was so tall that it dwarfed the men beside it, and each grain was larger than a man's head. Dozens of men were required to carry one ear of maize. Melons were larger than the houses. The more Li Chi thought of the painting, the more it bothered him.

At his group-discussion meeting that night, Li Chi was asked to describe what he had seen at the collective farm in terms that applied to the "red and expert" principle. On impulse, Li Chi decided to take a dangerous gamble that, if he lost, could mean catastrophe for him. He began with a brief account of his trip and a detailed description of the mural. "Since returning," Li Chi said then, "I have become convinced that when I neglected to criticize that painting, I was neither 'red' nor expert. I failed both in my duty as an artist and in my duty to the people." This comment, simply because it was outside the usual pattern, brought a hush of fear to his listeners. Nevertheless, Li Chi pushed on. "As an expert," he said, "I should have criticized the substitution of a crude, garish, and distracting picture for the purity of an undecorated whitewashed wall which would have been better for the digestion of those who dined there or for the powers of concentration of those who held meetings in the hall. I should have criticized the waste of the peasants' time in working on the picture. Because the colors were inexpertly mixed they were muddy and ugly, and as an artist I was shocked by the waste of gallons of paint when we professionals who would use it properly cannot get enough for our needs—"

A murmur of dissent came from the audience, and the cadre in charge suddenly said: "Stop! You speak from the lofty arrogance of a bourgeois critic. You demonstrate precisely why an expert must also be 'red.' Without redness, you are hostile to the people—blind."

"I am not a bourgeois," Li Chi said calmly, "and you people here are the only bourgeois I have known." This caused a gasp of horror from the listeners. "A bourgeois artist might well have found something appealing—certainly something unusual—in that primitive art, and I do not doubt that he would praise it.

But it is exactly because I am one of those people, while at the same time something of an expert in art, that I am aware of the falseness and wrongness of that painting."

"You say that because you are not adequately 'red,' " the cadre argued. "That's what is needed—to see the people's efforts through the eyes of a revolutionary who knows the true power of the masses—"

Li Chi shook his head. "On the basis of 'redness,' the mural should be criticized even more. It was not painted from a spontaneous feeling for decoration or self-expression on the part of the peasants. It was the idea of the farm's Party Secretary, who is an urban intellectual and who knows nothing of the peasant. He ordered the group of peasants from the fields, gave them the paint, and told them what to paint. He told us that he had done this in order to amuse us visiting delegates from the city."

"Now just a minute!" the cadre said, his voice shaking. "You've made an accusation there—a serious one. You have accused the Party of misguiding the peasants."

"I refuse to accept that the Party, or any other group, could guide our peasants to the extent of 'misguiding' them," Li Chi replied calmly. "But the peasants could be misinformed and confused so that they would be unable to perform their function with their customary efficiency."

"I warn you, Mr. Li Chi," the cadre said, "the Party will not stand for rightist lies and slander. If you are charging the Party with deliberately spreading confusion among the masses, you had better be able to substantiate your charges."

Li Chi was pale now, and he knew he was in trouble, but he forced himself to appear unperturbed and reasonable. "Naturally the Party Secretary doesn't mean to spread confusion, but it would be almost impossible for a city man from a distant part of the country not to have some misunderstandings in communicating with those peasants," Li Chi said. "The peasants are ignorant and simple people. Moreover, the Party propaganda has continually stressed the theme that the peasants are to avoid

61

superstition and fantasy. Nevertheless, the peasants I talked to had been told that, simply by accepting unquestioningly the Party's leadership, they will be assured the miracles they drew. In short, they believed literally the fantasies they were made to paint."

"Do you deny that the masses can accomplish miracles?" the cadre shouted.

"As a peasant myself, I have some notion of what they can and cannot accomplish," Li Chi said. "A miracle for our millions of peasants would be sufficient food every day. That would be a miracle they could understand and work hard to accomplish. But if they are allowed to believe that they can have sumptuous feasts every day simply by giving absolute obedience to a Party Secretary who knows nothing of agriculture, they will end up with even less than they have today. If I were truly 'red' and expert, I would have told the peasants that they could not eat the paint of that mural—and that the stuff of dreams is even less nourishing—"

At this, a storm of protest broke out from the group. "Are you an expert agronomist as well as a so-called art expert?" Li Chi heard the cadre shouting, "Or are you an expert troublemaker bent on promoting the counterrevolution of your rightist masters?" Taking this cue from "the authority," the others accused Li Chi of similar crimes. "Individualism," "anti-mass viewpoint," "rightism," "bourgeois treachery," "treason," and "slandering the noble qualities of our heroic Party cadres," were typical.

Finally he was sent out of the room and placed under house detention. Two burly cadres were put on guard over him and he was not permitted to leave his room until a group of officials in the Institute's Party apparatus had met to discuss his crime.

The next day he was called into a special meeting of his discussion group. The meeting was attended by the Party officials. Li Chi was further examined for his attitude on "red" and expert. He maintained his previous argument to the effect that, in his understanding of the term, he should have criticized the mural painted by the peasants, and he should have warned the peasants about the meaning of the picture.

When it was obvious that arguments would not change his opinion, his "case" was presented to the "masses," that is, to his fellow discussion-group members. As before, the others accused him of every possible crime, until the ones that the authorities had already decided upon were mentioned. These "crimes" were then taken up by the officials as representing the "will of the masses." The crimes included "willful obstinacy in accepting the mass viewpoint," "stubbornness in accepting the principle of 'red and expert,'" "failure to accept Party leadership," and "individualism."

Thereupon, the masses were asked to devise a suitable punishment. The suggestions went all the way from "a single death is too good for him" to "reprimand with the suggestion of further study on ideological subjects." The Party officials chose, as the will of the "masses," the punishment they and the other students considered the worst. Li Chi was sentenced for an "indefinite period of ideological remolding" to a newly organized farm cooperative in the distant wilderness of Sinkiang. Despite themselves, a barely audible moan of dismay came from the students.

Li Chi, however, could hardly believe his ears. His relief was so great and his delight so intense that he could not hide them. "Thank you, thank all of you," he said, his voice trembling with emotion. "As you know, I am a peasant. For a long time I have been homesick for a peasant's life and a peasant's work. I never asked to be an artist. I have never wanted to be one." He held up his big rough hands. "From now on I shall work with these in the honest soil of our motherland. I am going home."

There was a stunned silence. Li Chi's words had been completely unexpected, and yet the sincerity of them was unmistakable. The others understood that, far from being punished, the criminal was getting what he wanted most. A few of the more intelligent suspected that Li Chi had tricked them into it.

"Don't leap to conclusions," one Party cadre said. "We have invested much time and money in your art training and we do not intend to waste it. Your first job on that farm will be to paint scenes of socialist construction there. You will receive paper and paint and you will produce a stated amount of work. You will be permitted to indulge in farm labor only in your spare time."

This was more than Li Chi could have hoped for. He laughed aloud for sheer joy; then he bowed in mock subservience. "I bend to the will of the masses," he said. "I make myself a willing tool of the Party!"

CHAPTER V

{{

The Lanchow Sketches

On the evening before Li Chi left for Sinkiang, the members of his Institute discussion group gave him a farewell dinner. The next morning they saw him off at the station and presented him with a large red paper flower. The insincerity in these gestures was painfully obvious—Li Chi had had almost nothing in common with the other group members—but even worse was the official pretense that Li Chi had been given a great privilege in being sent to do manual labor in the wilderness and that therefore he was some kind of pioneer-hero.

On the train, the two cadres in charge of the group being sent to Sinkiang scrupulously maintained another pretense. In relays, they harangued the prisoners. The gist of their talk was that the prisoners were on their way to a sort of paradise on earth, a garden spot supplied with every comfort where with little effort a group of happy people lived in joyous harmony.

The purpose of the pretense apparently was partly to falsify the records for posterity and partly to save face for the Party leaders, or perhaps even to allow the leaders to delude themselves. In reality, of course, the punitive nature of the group's assignment to Sinkiang was unmistakable. Except for Li Chi, the prisoners were soft-handed, middle-class intellectuals. They knew they were going into a harsh wilderness from which they probably would never return. They would live in crowded barracks; they would be given a barely adequate quantity of the coarsest food; and they would be made to work hard twelve hours a day, seven days a week. Hence they either closed their ears to the cadres' words or, in listening, allowed the words to feed inner fires of hatred and bitterness.

None of this applied to Li Chi. He did not even consider himself an exile. He had known hardship most of his life, and he was not afraid of it. Moreover, because his first duty would be to paint pictures, he would not be required to do too much heavy labor. Finally, he did not doubt that, if and whenever he desired, he could contrive to get away from Sinkiang. What he expected to find at the cooperative farm was contact once again with people who lived in direct touch with nature—his kind of people—and at the same time to escape the complexities, insecurity, and the pretenses of a Party-controlled urban society. These expectations, plus the fact that he had a month's supply of paper and paints, made him the one happy person in the crowded "hard seat" carriage that rattled its way toward the distant western wilderness.

After two days, the train reached Lanchow. This was a frontier town and represented the easy first third of their journey. Beyond Lanchow the trains rarely ran to a fixed schedule, and Li Chi's group, therefore, settled down on the station platform for a long wait. Two hours later they were told that the delay would last several days at least and that they would have to spend the time at the station.

Li Chi went to the two cadres and announced casually that he was going to do some sight-seeing in the town. The cadres were speechless with surprise. The fact that they were guards and that their charges were prisoners was understood by everyone, and everyone acted accordingly. It was only a pretense that the cadres were humble guides and that the exiles were heroic volunteers with the liberty to do whatever they wanted. Because previously in their experience no one had ever dared to take advantage of the pretense, the cadres did not know how to handle the situation. They tried to protest—they told Li Chi that he might get lost or that he might miss his food ration—but Li Chi only laughed at them. Nevertheless, Li Chi knew that he must give them a means of saving face. He therefore pointed out that his assignment required him to paint pictures and that he ought to look the town over for possible paint-worthy subjects. This confused the guards even more; and Li Chi walked away before they could think of some other excuse to stop him. Nothing infuriated Party cadres more than to have their pretenses used against them, however, and Li Chi realized as he left that he had made enemies of the two guards.

He forgot the guards, however, in his delight with the town of Lanchow. To him, it was fascinatingly foreign. Also, he had not realized that so many of the Hui (Chinese Muslims) lived in the area. The facial structure and expressions of these people, especially of the elderly and the very young, were a stimulating challenge, and his fingers itched to sketch them. Finally, he could resist no longer. He sat down with his notebook in a small market square and in a moment was absorbed in his work.

Twenty minutes later he was interrupted by a tap on his shoulder. He looked up into the pinched, bespectacled face of a typical fanatic Party cadre. The cadre snapped his fingers, pointed to the notebook, and demanded it wordlessly with an arrogant gesture. "Go away," Li Chi said.

The scrawny little Party worker obviously was not used to being addressed in that tone of voice, and he lost his temper. He demanded Li Chi's notebook and tried to take it out of Li Chi's hand. Li Chi held the notebook out of the man's reach and threatened him with bodily injury if the cadre did not depart. The man did leave, but Li Chi was unable to continue his sketching because the square now was deserted. A moment later, the cadre returned with two policemen who lifted Li Chi up and marched him to a police station. The particulars of his identity were taken, and he was left alone in a small room that was bare except for a battered desk and two rickety chairs. To pass the time, Li Chi drew from memory a caricature of the cadre who had arrested him. This was the first time Li Chi had been in trouble with the police, and he was a little worried. He sensed, however, that self-confidence and an attitude of righteous indignation would be his best defense.

Fifteen minutes later, three men entered the room. The first was the wizened little cadre from the market square, the second was one of the overseer guards from the group at the station, and the third was a tall slender man in his forties; he was, Li Chi assumed correctly, a police official.

The tall man sat down at the desk and studied Li Chi briefly. "According to Comrade Kuo here," the policeman said finally, indicating the little cadre with the glasses, "you are an imperialist agent or perhaps only a counterrevolutionary. On the other hand," the policeman continued, "Comrade Chiang here says you are an escapee from the group he is taking into Sinkiang. Just what are you?"

"I'm an artist," Li Chi said. The policeman seemed basically friendly, and Li Chi therefore was able to speak calmly. "And as an artist," he went on, "I would be flattered to show my work to anyone who expressed a desire to see it. Your Comrade Kuo, however, did not ask to see my sketches. He tried to take them from me. He acted with such insolence, such arrogance, I could not imagine that he was a Party cadre. In fact, I thought that somehow this part of our country was still not liberated and that it was in control of KMT Nationalist officers—"

Comrade Kuo gasped and pointed dramatically at Li Chi.

"Slander of noble qualities of Party cadres," he shouted. "Obstructing heroic Party cadres in performance of duties. Failure to give heart to Party. Detaches himself from organization. Detaches himself from *Party*—"

"Disregard of organization. Disregard of *discipline*—" Comrade Chiang from the group at the station interrupted to say. He made no effort to hide the pleasure he felt because Li Chi was in trouble.

"Disregard of mass viewpoint," Comrade Kuo continued, disregarding the interruption. *"Puts himself in opposition to Party."*

"That's enough," the police officer said. The room became silent immediately. The officer turned to Li Chi. "Would you give *me* the pleasure of seeing your notebook?" he asked.

"The pleasure is mine," Li Chi said, handing over the book. The officer studied each sketch carefully. When he came to the one of Comrade Kuo, the corners of his mouth, Li Chi saw, twitched into a smile.

"Just as I feared," the officer said. "You drew mostly the faces of the Hui."

"It's a trick. Maybe it's a code—" the cadre Kuo said, but the officer pretended not to hear.

"You must understand that the Hui are a minority people," the officer continued. "They tend toward backwardness. It's not their fault. The exploiting classes of the past are to blame. Nevertheless, our invincible Communist Party under the inspired leadership of Chairman Mao has liberated the Hui. Understandably, the simple people have opened their hearts in love for the Party and our all-wise, all-merciful Chairman Mao, but—"

Li Chi leaned forward to hear what would follow. Like everyone else on the mainland, he was completely accustomed to the Communists' habit of using a propaganda barrage to precede any statement that might be taken to suggest a small error or shortcoming of the regime.

69

"—but sometimes, in their backwardness, they fail to see the advantages of accepting fully our guidance in the glorious task of socialist construction."

"You can't really blame them," Li Chi said, "if Comrade Kuo treats them with the same lofty bourgeois bureaucratism that he treats a fellow Han Chinese."

"I protest the slander of this masked counterrevolutionary," Kuo shouted.

The officer slapped the desk with his hand; he did not look at Kuo, but the gesture was enough to cut off the little man's further recriminations. "We are discussing the problem of *you*," the officer said to Li Chi. "The religion of the Hui forbids them to draw pictures of human beings. Sometimes they take offense at being photographed. They may be angered because of your sketching them. Even now they may be preparing another of their innumerable complaints because of you. If so, we shall not take kindly to your having left the railway station and the supervision of Comrade Chiang." The officer stood up and slipped Li Chi's notebook into his pocket.

Li Chi's earlier anxiety returned. He saw that the two cadres were gloating triumphantly.

"On the other hand," the policeman said, "one can never really tell what the Hui will do. It happens that one of them who is a *very* high Party official is presently visiting us. I'll show him your sketches tonight. We'll leave the decision up to him." At the door he turned back. "Meanwhile, you will remain with us," he said, and departed.

Shortly thereafter Li Chi's belongings were brought and thrown into his room. Later, a small bowl of simple food was given to him. Li Chi was aware of some nagging apprehension, but he refused to let himself become frightened. He managed to sleep well enough despite the hard floor.

In the morning, to his surprise, a sumptuous meal was brought to him, including fruit, which was rare indeed. He had scarcely finished when several people bustled in. The police official introduced Li Chi to the "very high" Hui Party Secretary, a portly little gray-haired man dressed in natty foreign clothes.

"I have come here personally," the Party Secretary said, "to tell you how much I enjoyed your sketches. They're charming —but *charming.* You have remarkable talent, dear boy. I've studied in Europe, and I know something of art."

"I hope I did not offend the good people here," Li Chi said.

"Offend? Nonsense!" the Party Secretary said. "They're flattered. In fact, if you would do some finished pictures of my people it would help their morale."

"I would like to very much," Li Chi said.

"Excellent, my boy," the older man said. "Your group won't get train accommodations to Sinkiang for another week. We'll see that you have a place to work and a guide to take you around." He handed Li Chi the notebook, gave him a smile, and was gone.

The police official shook Li Chi's hand warmly. "If there is anything we can do to help," he said, "just ask."

"Perhaps Comrade Chiang will fetch my things from the station," Li Chi said.

Chiang leaped forward; he was beaming. "It's an honor to serve a great people's artist, a hero of socialist construction," he said.

"And you," Li Chi said, pointing to Comrade Kuo. "Fetch me a pedicab."

"At once, sir," Kuo answered; he was actually trembling with eagerness. "Consider me naught but a humble machine, the one function of which is to do your bidding."

The police officer regarded this scene with open mouth. "You know what I think, Mr. Li Chi?" he said then. "I think it's high time you became a Party member."

CHAPTER VI

Red Smoke

By noon, Li Chi had moved into his own room. It seemed to be in a warehouse, but it was clean, airy, the light was good, and it was closer to the center of town. Just as he was about to leave for more sketching, there was a knock on his door. He opened it to a young Hui girl of about twenty who looked at him shyly. "I am Ka Lo," she said. "I was sent, please, to guide you—"

Li Chi could not help himself; he laughed aloud

"Please," she said, "did I do something wrong?" She seemed close to tears.

"It's your accent," Li Chi said. He took her arm and brought her into the room. "I have never heard our language spoken that way."

"I speak badly, I know," she said, turning her head away.

"No, no!" he said. "Your voice is music and you speak the language precisely as it should be spoken. I'm the one with the bad accent."

"I'm so ashamed," she said.

Her eyes, large and lustrous, were even lovelier than her voice, he thought. Her face was round, but she was more slender than Miss Fei had been. He wanted to laugh again for pure joy.

That afternoon, Ka Lo proved how useful she could be. She showed him places of special interest and she introduced him to important personages among her people. When he saw someone he wanted to sketch, she arranged the matter so tactfully that the model, whether a dignified old man or a restless little girl, posed willingly. By early evening, he had enough sketches. They hurried back to his room where he began to paint quickly in order not to waste any of the daylight. Ka Lo watched for a while and then went out for food, which she brought back and prepared in his room. After they had eaten, she left.

For the next few days, Li Chi lived in a kind of trance. He was absorbed completely in his painting. With the first light of dawn he was at his worktable. Ka Lo arrived an hour or two later to prepare his breakfast. After eating, they would set out on an excursion she had planned carefully in advance. Twice they took picnic lunches and went into the countryside. Li Chi found that he had an almost overpowering desire to communicate through his watercolors his sense of wonder and fascination with this wild harsh land and the grave, ruggedly dignified people who belonged to it. As soon as he finished one painting, he forgot it in his impatience to begin another. He was aware that he was doing the best work he had ever done.

He mentioned this to Ka Lo one evening, and she asked him why it was that he was doing his best work now, at this particular time. "Part of it is because I'm free for the first time to work without interruption," he said. "But another important part of it is you." They were standing by his worktable, and he saw her with sudden special clarity in the last light of evening. "It is because you are beautiful; I am inspired and I want to make my pictures beautiful—" But almost immediately he shook his head. "That's not right. It's because you're beautiful and I am

73

so *ugly,*" he began again. "I want to make my pictures so attractive you'll look at them and not at me."

"No, no!" she said. Her voice was shaking. "Please, you are not ugly. No one could ever think that."

She spoke with such conviction that Li Chi was overcome with affection for her. Without thinking, he hugged her. He found that they clung together, straining against each other. They broke apart almost at once, trembling and confused, and she ran out of the room.

The next evening she took him to a feast given by relatives of hers. Her father and uncles were Party members, and it was for this reason that she was permitted to be "progressive." At the same time, however, she was able to win the approval of her more conventional clansmen. Thus Li Chi found that he was welcome at the feast, and for the first time he felt completely at home with these people. Several times he could not resist sketching various members of the family, but he shared their gaiety equally with them.

The next morning when he went to his worktable he discovered to his horror that he was almost entirely out of paints. He had used up a whole month's supply in only six days. He checked again, and found that there was sufficient left for perhaps two rather skimpy pictures. He decided instead to use the remaining paint luxuriously on one large picture.

Perhaps because of the shortage, he took greater pains than usual. In any case, the picture he completed an hour later was easily the best he had ever painted, and he knew it would remain one of his masterpieces The faces, taken from the sketches he had drawn at the feast the night before, were shown reflected in the light of the fire on which the rich meat for the feast roasted. Somehow the light in them seemed to give the fire its brightness. The eager, mouth-watering delight of anticipating the succulent roast meat was plainly visible. Even more, however, the faces glowed with the happiness of a reunited family; they had seemingly drawn all reality around their little fire so

that the rest of the world appeared vague and insubstantial beyond the veil of red smoke. Li Chi studied the picture, awed by
it, even if he had painted it himself. In a final burst of inspiration the right title for it suggested itself to him: "Red Smoke."

He was impatient to show it to Ka Lo, but when she arrived a
few minutes later she wore such an air of tragedy that he forgot
everything else. When he pressed her to tell him what was
wrong, she suddenly burst into tears and buried her head in his
chest. His feelings were torn between distress at her suffering
and delight at holding her against him again. Finally, between
sobs, she revealed to him that his group had train accommodations to Sinkiang the next day. Moreover, the two guards had
been overheard discussing the plans they had for Li Chi on the
collective farm in Sinkiang. Li Chi understood suddenly that
once on the farm he would be almost entirely under the power
of two cadres who hated him and that therefore his chances of
survival would be slim. He found that he had lost all desire to
visit Sinkiang.

"Don't worry, we'll think of something," he said. "It won't be
easy," he added, "because I've run out of paints, and my only
excuse to stay here is as an artist."

Ka Lo leaned back, still in his arms, to look up into his face.
"You could use the vegetable dyes my people make," she said.
"But please, you must do something quickly."

Her concern for him touched him deeply. He could think of
no word to express his gratitude, and he therefore attempted to
communicate his emotion with a kiss. He was inept at it, and
together they groped toward each other awkwardly, but the
effect was satisfactory; both were left weak and shaky. As before, they were embarrassed and confused by the intensity of
their feelings, and their impulse was to run away from them in
fear.

Li Chi decided to discuss the problem of his Sinkiang assignment with the police official who had seemed sympathetic. He
took with him the impressive pile of paintings he had finished.

"Even I can tell that these are well done," the police official said, after looking at Li Chi's pictures. He held up "Red Smoke." "To me, this is a fine example of socialist realism. A group of our minority comrades who have seen the light—the *red* light—of socialist progress."

"You have the natural good taste of a professional critic," Li Chi said.

"I may know nothing about art," the official confessed modestly, "but I do know what I like."

"As you know, I am assigned to Sinkiang for the purpose of depicting the progress of socialist construction there in pictures like these," Li Chi said. "But unfortunately I've used up all my paint."

"Perhaps you should return to Peking for more," the official said.

"I had thought that perhaps a telegram could be sent to the Art Institute," Li Chi said. "The paint could be sent to me here by someone who could be coming anyway."

"That might save time," the officer admitted.

"And meanwhile I might profitably study the techniques whereby the Hui make their vegetable dyes."

"From the masses and to the masses," the policeman said approvingly, and added, "It might help matters if you would agree to give a lecture or two on art to the classes for Hui youngsters."

Li Chi said that he would be happy to oblige, and the policeman said he would be happy to send the necessary telegram. In conclusion, the officer said that he was happy to be of some small service in advancing the artistic front in the battle for socialist progress. "And I doubt if our people would see many more of your pictures if you went to Sinkiang," he said.

Li Chi shuddered. He was aware that he had had a narrow escape.

Back in his room, Ka Lo was waiting for him. She seemed as happy as he was that he would not be leaving immediately. In their joy, they attempted another kiss. This time they found that their skill had improved and that the effect was even more frighteningly tempestuous than before.

That afternoon, Ka Lo took Li Chi to a small hut near the edge of town. Hence she introduced him to an ancient witch who, he learned, was regarded locally as the top expert on herbs and dyes. The woman readily agreed to teach Li Chi what she could about her craft. Thereafter Li Chi, with Ka Lo as interpreter, met every day with the old woman. She took them on long excursions into the countryside to gather certain roots, berries, leaves, gums and clays. Back at the hut, Li Chi would write down the recipes as the old woman brewed her brightly colored dyes.

The old woman often spoke to Ka Lo in such a way as to make the girl blush and stammer in embarrassment. On the fourth day of his lessons in native dye craft, the old woman spoke to Li Chi in Mandarin, and although her accent was bad she made her meaning clear. She said that she knew nothing about politics but she understood all about love. She told him that when two young people were in love, there was only one thing that ought to be done about it. She then informed him that she was leaving him and Ka Lo alone in her hut for the rest of the afternoon in order that he could get on with what he ought to do about being in love. With that she nudged him, made a ribald gesture, and left. He heard the sound of her cackle fade to silence down the lane. Ka Lo could not look at him, but he saw that her hands were shaking as she fumbled with the top button of her blouse. Li Chi almost fainted with joy and sudden excitement. When the old witch returned that evening, she studied the young couple for a moment and then laughed, seemingly delighted with what she perceived.

Li Chi now lived in a kind of roseate dream. He experimented with the vegetable dyes, but he is credited with only one successful picture of this period, a portrait on silk of Ka Lo and the old woman together. With Ka Lo's help he memorized the words necessary to talk on art to classes of the Hui children. This was important because it helped Ka Lo with her job; as the daughter of a Party member she had received education and political indoctrination. Thus she was active in the Youth League and was assigned a propaganda function in persuading her people, especially the younger ones, to accept the "progressive viewpoint." At present, her viewpoint tended to be limited to Li Chi—they were alone together in the old woman's hut every afternoon—and his work with her pupils helped prevent any unpleasant gossip. Fortunately, the old woman was discreet, and the happiness of the young couple was complete.

Two weeks after he had begun to learn about vegetable dyes and love, Li Chi received a note from the police officer advising that the paints had arrived with a messenger who had instructions to take Li Chi's completed paintings back to Peking. Li Chi awoke from his dream. He was in agony at the thought of leaving Ka Lo. She also was heartbroken, and clung to him desperately. He put off going to the policeman's office as long as he could.

The police officer took him to the quarters of the cadre who had come from Peking. Li Chi gave his bundle of paintings to the man and asked for the supply of paints.

To Li Chi's surprise, the cadre replied, "I gave the paints to the children who came for them." When Li Chi showed his astonishment and demanded to know why the paints intended for him should be given to someone else, it was the cadre's turn to be astonished. "I naturally assumed the paints were intended for the children and that you had sent the children to pick up the package," he said. "See? They left me a copy of their school wall newspaper as a memento."

Li Chi took the paper, and the police officer, looking over Li Chi's shoulder, read the childishly formed characters aloud. "We are remembered by the kind Party uncles from Peking," the paper said. "All the way from Peking has come a fine present of beautiful paints just for us. To show our thanks we will paint in unforgettable hues the glorious message of the Communist Party and Chairman Mao Tse-tung who have shown such heartfelt sympathy for the minority youth. Thank you, Peking uncle!"

The police officer beamed. "I knew that you were having some success in cementing our relations with the minority people," he said to Li Chi, "but I never dreamed that it was this much. Peking will be delighted, I can tell you, to receive this little newspaper."

"But my paints—" Li Chi began.

The officer brushed it aside. "Some innocent misunderstanding," he said. "The children must have requested the paints. Otherwise how could they have expected them? We certainly could not take the paints away now—"

"But how can I fulfill my assigned tasks?" Li Chi wanted to know.

"Patience," the officer counseled. "Remember the Party's instructions, 'Discard the light load and take up the heavy; shun the easy task and pursue the difficult; deprive yourself to give to others.' " He put a fatherly hand on Li Chi's shoulder. "We will request another supply of paints for you, and meanwhile you can continue your excellent work with our minority peoples."

Back in his own room, Li Chi put Ka Lo on trial and demanded from her the whole truth and nothing but the truth. Thus when he asked her if she had had anything to do with the children's wall newspaper and the intercepting of the paints, she made a full confession. "But I did it only to keep you here a little longer," she pleaded. "And the children will let you have all the paint you want."

Nevertheless, he sentenced her to be struggled against. Moreover, when the sentence was being carried out she moaned piteously, but Li Chi did not feel that he was being hardhearted in the least.

CHAPTER VII

More Red Smoke

During the last half of 1958, the Peking leaders were especially concerned with the minorities problem. In dealing with the minorities, the Communists had gone to greater extremes in their customary fluctuation between leniency and suppression than they had in dealing with the Han. The result was that in some areas the minority groups were, in effect, absorbed and had become indistinguishable from the Han. In other areas—Tibet, for example—the people in every social stratum were resisting the obliteration of their national and cultural identity with such zeal and violence that the cost of socialist construction there was almost prohibitive. Moreover, the Hundred Flowers campaign had revealed that even in places where the assimilation seemed complete, hatred for the Han in general and the Party cadre Han in particular smoldered just below the surface.

The anti-rightist campaign, of course, had suppressed all outward manifestation of such feelings. Moreover, the subsequent campaigns had established officially that these feelings did not and never had existed. None of this subterfuge, however, removed the anxieties or overcame the insecurity of the Han officials who, in the name of the "people," lived in the minority areas and administered them. These anxieties, when passed up the chain of command to the appropriate top officials in Peking, became magnified. If the pretense of "felicitous fraternal love and cooperation between the Han and the minorities" should be exposed through any wide expression of the minority people's true feelings, nationwide morale would be lowered seriously and progress would be slowed down disastrously at home; abroad, the effect on the other peoples of Asia and on China's foreign relations generally might be even worse.

This explains why Li Chi's simple ability to get along with the Hui was given inflated importance in certain quarters in Peking. Li Chi's earlier success with painting minority types during the Dalai Lama's visit was recalled, and he was credited with being an expert in dealing with minority peoples. The fact was, however, that the majority of the Hui in Lanchow were outwardly no different from the Han. Like the Han, they were made to express over and over again ardent, unfaltering love for socialism, the Party, Chairman Mao, and the local Party officials. On their own time, however, they were not made to manifest love for anyone, and if there was anyone for whom they then made less effort to manifest love, it was a nonofficial Han. Hence Li Chi did represent an exception. The fact that the Hui showed affection for Li Chi without being forced to do so proved that their affection was genuine. And if the Hui could genuinely like one Han, they might learn to like two—or even several. The possibilities were electrifying.

Understandably, the Lanchow administrators, for their own benefit, exploited the anxieties of their superiors. Thus it was they who reported to Peking on Li Chi's success in winning the affection of the local Hui. In making the report, they claimed part of the credit for the success, because it was they who first recognized Li Chi's capability and saw to it that he was maneuvered into the position from which the achievement was possible. When this approach obtained favorable response from above, the Lanchow officials wrote more of the same, and they exaggerated.

Before long, therefore, a number of personages in Peking had begun to regard Li Chi's friendship with a few Hui as a major breakthrough in the wall of distrust that, propaganda to the contrary, existed between the Han and the minorities people. These personages regarded Li Chi with increasing approbation. From their viewpoint, he seemed to have everything: the proper class origin, intelligence, genuine talent, and above all the ability to project for once a *desirable* image of the Han to the non-Han. Desks were pounded in Peking on the subject of Li Chi, and a frequently heard question was, "Why isn't that man in the Party?"

Inevitably, the research on Li Chi's record revealed that the "masses," that is, his fellow discussion-group members, had convicted him of political crimes and had sentenced him, as far as the authorities were concerned, to death. The high-level officials, however, did not fool themselves about the role of the masses in Li Chi's conviction; they put the blame entirely on the Party cadres at the Art Institute. Institute officials were forced to blacken Li Chi's character in order to justify their punishment of him, and the more they were criticized, the more they insisted that Li Chi was an unregenerate criminal. Admittedly, their case against him was weak. His previous record had been flawless; therefore the fact that he should suddenly turn out to be a dangerous rightist just was not believable. The superior authorities reasoned that when Li Chi erred about the "red and expert" principle he proved merely that his indoctrination had been inadequate; to send him to Sinkiang for this was like mercy-killing a patient who had only a slight cold. Stung by such accusations, the authorities at the Art Institute insisted that Li Chi was a political leper who needed to be quarantined. This argument over Li Chi became steadily more acrimonious,

82

and it spread slowly as a wider group of high officials took sides in the controversy.

Luckily, Li Chi was blissfully unaware that he was the cause of a distant conflict. Innocently, he thought that he had been forgotten; he was happy to live for nothing but the moments he could spend with Ka Lo. Li Chi's dalliance with the pretty Hui girl lasted eleven weeks. It ended abruptly in late August, 1958, with a telegram ordering him to return at once to Peking, where he was to "claim proper recognition for the painting of a masterpiece of socialist art, 'Red Smoke.' "

The thought of leaving Ka Lo, however, was unendurable. He could not ask her to marry him, because he did not even have a job. He did beg her, however, to wait for him; he swore that somehow he would manage to return to Lanchow with the means to making a living. Ka Lo was more realistic. Sadly but firmly she made him accept that once he had left, the chances of their ever seeing each other again were slight. She told him that her ancestors had been nomads and that they had evolved a philosophy which was helpful in times like these. People who always were on the move could not become attached to any one locality. Hence, they learned not to think of the past; they lived instead only for the present, grateful for the moments of happiness, and hoping for good fortune, rich pastures, and pleasant weather in the next place they pitched their tents. Li Chi and Ka Lo parted sadly, but without excessive sentimentality.

On the train to Peking, Li Chi began to anticipate his return with increasing excitement. He had no objection to fame and fortune, and because he himself knew that his painting "Red Smoke" was good, he could feel that he was not undeserving of just about as much as the authorities could offer in the way of reward and praise. He began to prepare statements to use when he was interviewed by journalists or officials.

No journalists or officials awaited him at the Peking station, however; in fact, he was met by no one. He was a little disappointed, but as he made his way toward the Art Institute he chided himself for expecting and wanting something that he had never desired before in his life.

It was late afternoon when Li Chi arrived at the familiar place. Here, at least, he found that he was expected. A janitor recognized him and led him, not to the students' dormitory, but to one of the rooms for instructors. It was a room for two instead of for six. The other occupant was not in. On the unassigned bed Li Chi found a note addressed to him; it instructed him to attend a group-discussion meeting that, he noticed, was scheduled to have begun several minutes previously. He threw his belongings on the cot and went at once in search of the meeting room.

He entered the room quietly. Unobtrusively he took a seat at the back. No one had been speaking at the moment, however, and everyone turned around to look at him silently. The group was unusually large. It included most of the instructors and professors he had known previously, plus a few new faces and an impressive number of Party functionaries.

A departmental Party Secretary stood up; he announced that the special meeting now could come to order and that its purpose was to "examine and criticize a watercolor called 'Red Smoke' that had been painted by an erstwhile student of the Institute." The painting was produced and hung upon the wall. Li Chi felt a thrill of pride and anticipation.

It was short lived. To his astonishment, his fellow artists attacked his picture more viciously than he had ever before heard a painting criticized. The style, they said, was inappropriate to the subject; the technique was inadequate, amateurish, and vulgar. Proportion and balance were badly off. Color and color contrasts violated every aspect of good taste. And, in summary, the picture as a whole demonstrated bourgeois influence of the most degenerate variety.

At first, Li Chi could hardly believe his ears. Then he was stung by the criticisms. Soon, however, he began to recover. What they said, he realized, was not only unjust, it was untrue;

he knew it and he knew that the others knew it as well. That meant that his picture had become entangled in political controversy. He now began to listen for political overtones in the criticism.

His earlier failure to understand and appreciate the principle of "red and expert" was recalled; his painting was cited as a ghastly example of what could happen to the work of an artist who thought that he could become "expert" without developing political awareness, or "redness." Except for this, however, the criticisms adhered to the technical and artistic aspect of his work. At the end of the meeting, Li Chi was presented as such a disgrace to the Institute that his case was without precedent. The decision on what should be done would require careful consideration. Meanwhile, Li Chi was to be confined to quarters. Back in his room, Li Chi went through alternate fits of anger, anxiety, and depression.

The other occupant of the room was of that ubiquitous cadre type: scrawny, humorless, self-righteous, and tireless in his political activity. In the room he acted as though Li Chi had a contagious loathsome disease. Most of the time he sat silently and stared at Li Chi; he held a poised pen and a notebook in which he ostentatiously from time to time took down notations of Li Chi's behavior.

At first the cadre refused to speak to Li Chi at all. The little man lacked intelligence, however, and with a little verbal needling Li Chi was able to sting the cadre into some unguarded comments. From these, Li Chi deduced the following aspects concerning his predicament. First, he was well regarded by certain high Party men in the Propaganda Department and in the department responsible for minority affairs. Second, these personages had been highly critical of the Art Institute's Party cadres who had failed in their indoctrination duties by not making Li Chi into a Party member and, worse, had stupidly wasted Li Chi's talents by sentencing him to manual labor in Sinkiang. Three, the Institute Party men were protecting themselves by blackening Li Chi's character. And four, this issue had come down to a struggle between the pro–Li Chi and the anti–Li Chi groups concerning the admission of his Lanchow watercolors into a certain exhibition. The exhibition was to be part of a general tribute the Propaganda Department was paying to the minority peoples. For the exhibition, various known artists had been commanded to paint pictures delineated by Propaganda Department cadres; Li Chi guessed that these "commercial" works, however, would have the stale triteness that invariably identified such projects. In comparison, therefore, Li Chi was not conceited in concluding that his genuinely inspired watercolors would stand out sharply. In this case, most of the prestige for the exhibition would accrue to him. Such prestige was sure to include the congratulations and therefore the approbation of the top leadership. This in turn would ensure the authenticity of Li Chi's genius and of his position as a people's artist. All those who had slandered him would be discredited.

The one weakness of the pro–Li Chi force was that none of the members were art experts. Exploiting this fact, the anti–Li Chi group attacked the technical and artistic quality of his work. Moreover, they were smart enough not to slash at all his paintings; instead they concentrated on cutting up his best one, the inference being that his others were not even worthy of their notice. Li Chi realized that, after the discussion meeting on "Red Smoke," any non-expert on art would have to have phenomenal self-confidence to choose any Li Chi painting for public display. It seemed to him that the group who favored him were at a disadvantage.

Li Chi waited two days under the unflinching stare of his cadre roommate. On the third day he was called to attend another group meeting. This one was conducted by a different Party Secretary—one who immediately demonstrated sympathy for Li Chi. He announced that a decision concerning the merit or otherwise of the painting "Red Smoke" had not been reached nor had the group come to any agreement on what should be done about the artist. Thus, he said, Li Chi himself was to be examined as a means of bringing more light to bear upon the problem. As a beginning, Li Chi was asked to describe the circumstances under which he had been sentenced to the Sinkiang wilderness.

Li Chi realized he was being given a rare chance for revenge upon the fellow artists who, in the "red and expert" meeting three months previously, had been made to turn upon him. He could sense now the hostility and fear from the artistic segment of his audience. None of his listeners, however, was prepared for what he said.

"I must set the record straight on one matter," he began. "I was not 'sentenced' to the collective farm in Sinkiang. My assignment had nothing to do with punishment or discipline. As you know, I come from the background of a poor peasant. I was the only one in my group at the Institute with such a background. It was deemed appropriate, therefore, that I should apply my talents and training to the task of depicting socialist construction in the countryside. In fact, I insisted upon it and would have been disappointed if the opportunity had been denied to me. I was especially glad for the honor of being the first people's artist to have the chance of painting scenes of the Sinkiang frontier. Any of you who attended the meeting at which I was given my assignment will recall, I'm sure, the sincerity of my happiness at receiving it. As it happened, because of other work which for the moment was deemed to have higher priority, I never reached Sinkiang. This has been something of a personal disappointment to me, and I sincerely hope that my chance to paint in Sinkiang has not been entirely lost."

Li Chi sat down, and for a moment the listeners were silent, presumably overcome momentarily with surprise. Then a murmur rose from the audience as the people began to whisper among themselves. Finally, one of the Party officials stood up.

"In the light of Mr. Li Chi's words," he said, "I suggest that we postpone this meeting while a reconsideration is made by the proper authorities."

Li Chi was fairly confident that his ploy would be successful. By denying that his original discussion-group cadres had punished him in any way, those cadres could not be criticized by the propaganda and minorities department officials. This then would remove the need for the Institute cadres to be critical of him. Back in his room, Li Chi still endured the silent scrutiny of the cadre, but he managed to get a good night's sleep

Li Chi had estimated correctly that his speech would remove the cause of conflict between the Institute authorities and the propaganda and minorities department officials. At the reconvened meeting the next morning, a new feeling of accord was easily apparent. Li Chi also was aware that the antagonism to him personally had vanished.

One aspect of the situation, however, had not been anticipated by Li Chi. When his supporters from the departments of propaganda and minority affairs lost their reason to be critical of the Institute authorities, they also lost any right to reject the Institute's denouncement of his painting. Hence it now looked as though he had succeeded only in lining up both groups against him instead of for him. At least, however, he was given a chance to answer the criticism of "Red Smoke."

This was a subject on which he had prepared no speech. "I must strenuously object to and reject the charge made here that my picture 'Red Smoke' represents bourgeois degeneracy in technique," Li Chi began. "I come from the poor peasantry and never had any contact whatever with the bourgeois. My entire training in art has been at this Institute where the vigilance against bourgeois influences has been constant and thorough. Hence to say that I have been bourgeois-influenced to the point of degeneracy is absurd." These were strong words and they caused a gasp from his listeners, but they did not refute the technical criticisms of his painting. How could he refute such criticism? It represented a value judgment that could not in any way be subjected to a scientific testing. Li Chi paused to collect his thoughts, and on impulse decided to act upon a hunch. The hunch concerned very discreet but persistent rumors that had been circulating for the past month or so and that concerned a possible ideological rift with Russia. "I do concede, however, that the style or technique I used in this picture might shock some of my Institute confreres," he went on. "As you all know, emulation of our Soviet elder brothers has been a firm policy applied to almost every aspect of our socialist construction program. In art, certainly, we all have tended to follow unquestioningly the leadership of our brother artists in the Soviet Union. I do not for a moment question the greater revolutionary experience of our Soviet elder brothers. Equally, I am aware that they are more advanced than we are in modern science and technology. As a simple peasant—one of the masses—however, I cannot feel that we Han need to follow anyone in the field of art. Thus, as you will notice in this painting, I have attempted to give increased realism to a concrete situation by adapting some of the proven techniques of our old masters to a progressive use of modern materials. . . ."

Again, Li Chi's words caused an uneasy stir within his audience. While Li Chi waited tensely, a number of whispered consultations were held. If the rumors of a Sino-Soviet conflict were true, Li Chi thought, a policy directive to cease emulating the Russians wherever possible would in all likelihood have gone out from the Chinese Communist leaders. If such a directive had been issued, rejecting Li Chi's comments would also mean disobeying the directive.

Finally, the Institute's top art expert and critic got slowly to his feet. Li Chi had always considered him an old fool—a man who knew all about art but who did not know what he liked. The Communists therefore gave him nominal authority and used him as a mouthpiece to express what *they* liked—and did not like—in art. "Upon giving this painting the benefit of a somewhat closer scrutiny," the old man said in his quavering voice, "certain hitherto unperceived aspects of the artist's technique are brought to light. Brushwork, for example, is revealed to be not without proficiency. Color values, while avoiding the garishness of some of our more exuberant moderns, eschew at the same time the banalities of the ancients—"

He was interrupted by one of the departmental Party Secretaries. "What I want to know is, can that painting be called a 'masterpiece of socialist realism,' a 'flawless example of the people's art'?"

The old critic blinked. "Such an evaluation would not be without merit," he said finally.

The audience milled around Li Chi, congratulating him and shaking his hand. Back in his room, the cadre roommate busied himself by washing Li Chi's underwear and brushing his clothes. He cringed whenever Li Chi looked at him, and his pen and notebook were nowhere in evidence.

Fortunately, however, Li Chi was soon so busy helping with the arrangements for the exhibition that he seldom saw his roommate. The exhibition opened, and he had the pleasure of being complimented and congratulated by high officials. At the Institute he was assigned temporarily to work with the faculty on the curriculum for the coming term.

Late in the afternoon of the third day of the exhibition, Li Chi returned to his room to find that all his paintings from the exhibition except "Red Smoke" were stacked on his bed. His roommate informed him with a sneer that he was to attend a special meeting of his group. The roommate once more treated him like a syphilitic, and followed him with pen poised over a notebook.

At the meeting, "Red Smoke" was again on display. The old art critic got slowly to his feet. "I wish to go a bit deeper into our critical analysis of this so-called painting," he began. "A painting has to *say* something. It must have a *soul*. In a progressive socialist society, we use the excellent expression 'political content.' Without political content, painting is a criminal waste of time, energy, and materials—"

As the meeting progressed, Li Chi finally learned that, earlier in the afternoon, an important Minister, one who had been on the Long March, had attended the exhibition and had paused briefly in front of "Red Smoke." "Weak politically," he had remarked about the picture. "Everyone knows the stupid Hui think of nothing but filling their guts, so why paint a picture of it?"

By the end of the meeting, Li Chi was once again a disgrace to the Institute. He was relieved of his duties on the faculty and was confined to his room until reassignment could be worked out.

At noon the next day, however, his door burst open and a crowd of people broke in. They shook his hand and congratulated him, then took him and his paintings to a special meeting of his group. "Red Smoke" was again put on display. "It is always a pleasure for me to discuss this delightful painting," the old critic began. "Not only is it executed brilliantly, but even more important it is rich in political content. Anyone who looks at this picture must be deeply touched by the generosity and consideration of us Han in seeing that our minority peoples are well fed and kept happy—"

Later in the meeting Li Chi learned that this evaluation of his picture had been expressed tersely and officially by the Acting Director of the Propaganda Department himself. "You just had a bit of bad luck, but it's all right now," the others in the group told Li Chi. "Your painting has top official approval, and nothing can change its status again."

They were wrong. Three days later Li Chi returned to his room to find his paintings piled on his bed again. The cadre once more wore a silent sneer, and Li Chi attended still another special meeting on "Red Smoke."

This time, the poor old critic was not made publicly to eat his previous words again. Instead, a genuinely frightened party official addressed the grave group. Li Chi learned that Chairman Mao Tse-tung himself had made one of his rare public appearances and had attended the exhibition early that afternoon. The great leader had made no comments about any of the paintings but he had stopped in front of "Red Smoke" and had belched. The matter was discussed at length in the attempt to determine what the belch had meant in terms of art criticism. One faction was of the opinion that in this context a belch would constitute a beautifully tactful, exquisitely laconic, but powerfully emphatic expression of disgust. A larger faction was not sure. One person suggested timidly that the painting might show the succulent roasting meat with such vivid reality that it could have a burp-like physical reaction on one who looked at it; the others, however, tended to the view that Li Chi wasn't *that* good.

The final decision was that a request would be set in motion up through the chain of command to reach the Party Chairman's dizzy pinnacle and to find out what precisely the belch had meant. Meanwhile the safest course would be to release Li Chi of his job, confine him to his room, and keep him under surveillance.

Four days later the reply filtered down through the cloud cap that obscured the Everest of Chinese Communist authority. The message was that, on the afternoon of the state visit, Chairman Mao had been preoccupied by profound matters of state policy. Thus he did not even remember the painting under discussion. Of course, the fact that he had ever belched was denied, and it was suggested that the person who had started the rumor that the Chairman had belched was trying to undermine the nation's morale by suggesting that the leader's health was poor; obviously such a rumormonger was an incorrigible rightist who should be identified and sent to labor reform at once.

By the end of that meeting the decision was that the Chairman's failure even to remember "Red Smoke" constituted condemnation of the picture. The next day, fortunately, the Acting

Propaganda Director once again took it upon himself to order Li Chi's painting returned to the exhibition.

Li Chi, however, had had enough. He remembered as a dream of paradise the weeks in Lanchow when the only thinking he did was to plan new forms of caresses to try on Ka Lo. His desire to get away from Peking had once again become overpowering. He asked for an appointment with the Propaganda Department official who was in charge of the exhibition.

Two days later, Li Chi was shown into the official's office. Li Chi discussed his feelings honestly with the older man and asked if there were some way whereby he, Li Chi, could withdraw his paintings from the exhibition and thereby remove the one reason why he had to stay in the capital.

"I'm glad you asked me that," the official said, picking up a note from his desk. "I've just had orders from our Director to remove your paintings from the exhibition and return them to you. It seems that representatives from the other minority groups have complained loudly about the preference shown for the Hui as indicated by the excessive number of pictures favoring them."

Li Chi groaned.

The official nodded in sympathy. " 'Red Smoke' is the real offender in this case," the official said. "It makes the Hui look so well fed and happy that naturally the others are jealous."

"I ought to tear it up," Li Chi said.

"No, no, no!" the official replied. "I have a better idea. You've no doubt heard that the masses are preparing for a gigantic effort to overcome the technological barrier. An important part of the effort will be small backyard steel furnaces that we will have the masses build—I mean, that the masses will spontaneously build. Why don't you change the cooking fire in your picture to a small smelter? Then the picture will show the true happiness of the people when they see molten slag and know that they are contributing to socialist construction."

Li Chi was horrified, but he managed to hold himself in check and to explain that such an attempt would ruin the picture. Seeing the official's disappointment, however, Li Chi offered to paint the same picture over again, substituting the small smelter for the cooking fire.

The official brightened. "If you do that," he said, "I'll take care of 'Red Smoke' for you." His suggestion, which Li Chi accepted gladly, was to send "Red Smoke" with a selection of other Chinese paintings, old and new, to a requested exhibition being put on in one of the socialist fraternal countries. "Albania, I think it's called," the official said.

Back at the Institute, Li Chi went at once to the Party Secretary of the administrative staff of the Institute and requested a job assignment posting. Li Chi's current status, as far as the Secretary had been instructed, was high. Thus he gave Li Chi a list of job openings and told Li Chi he could have his choice. "Pick the one you want and write to the appropriate secretary saying you are taking the post and telling him when you'll start work." He gave Li Chi a note of authority to include with the letter.

The first four jobs on the list were instructorships at the Institute. Li Chi knew that the Party Secretary expected him to take one of these. At the very bottom of the list was the job of art teacher for a small normal college in Wuhu, in his own depressed and often calamity-stricken province of Anhwei. This posting promised the least interference from Peking, Li Chi felt, and this was the one he chose. He wrote the letter accepting the post; before enclosing the Party Secretary's note of authority, Li Chi used it to draw the funds for traveling expenses. He spent the rest of the afternoon trying to duplicate "Red Smoke" with a smelter instead of a cooking fire. The result was far from successful, but he delivered it to the propaganda officer and went to the station to get a train reservation for the trip to Wuhu.

The earliest reservation he could get was for two days hence. Late the next afternoon, Li Chi's cadre roommate burst in with

94

a reproachful look on his face. "You chose the posting in *Wuhu*," he said, his voice expressing both astonishment and disgust. "Just when you reached a high tide of success with your smelter painting. Everyone is praising you. To the Hui goes the honor of being the first among the minorities to build a backyard furnace."

Li Chi said goodbye to no one, and left the Institute at a time when everyone was busy. On the station he hid himself within the crowds until only a few minutes before departure time. Subconsciously, he had known it would happen: just as he sat down he saw his cadre roommate struggling through the crowd toward him. Li Chi held his breath. The train started to move. The cadre spotted him; he ran alongside the train. "Come back!" he shouted. "Come back immediately! There is a special meeting. The Hui have never built a backyard furnace. The other minorities are furious. Your painting is a lie! One death is too good for a rightist like you!"

Li Chi put a hand behind his ear, pretending he could not hear. Then he nodded, smiled, and waved.

The cadre stopped running. "You belong in the Sinkiang wilderness—that's where you would have been sent," he shouted, and then shook his fist.

Li Chi pretended that the cadre was waving goodbye. Li Chi smiled again and leaned out the window to wave a final farewell.

CHAPTER VIII

The Potato Pit

Li Chi arrived in Wuhu the middle of September, 1958. He was met at the station by Mr. Wei, a stooped, shy little man ten years older than Li Chi. Mr. Wei would share a room with Li Chi and would be Li Chi's superior in what could laughingly be called the Art Department of the Normal College in Wuhu. Nevertheless, the little man was humble in his awe of Li Chi as a graduate of the Art Institute in Peking; obviously Li Chi would have to take whatever initiative was needed in running the department.

To Li Chi's surprise, however, no one else on the faculty was impressed with his achievements; in fact he was treated coolly, if not with actual disdain. The truth was that, having been rejected for posts of their choice and assigned to Wuhu Normal because either their qualifications or their class backgrounds were unacceptable for anything better, his colleagues assumed that Li Chi was in the same circumstances. Furthermore, Li Chi's position did not improve when it became known that his class background was impeccable and that his artistic ability had already received national acclaim. These facts rendered him only the more suspect, because assignment to Wuhu could only mean that he was a political outcast. It was inconceivable that he had chosen the post. Thus, the reaction of the others was that any social contact with him could only contaminate. Li Chi saw that he would have plenty of time for his students and his painting.

His students, however, required little attention. Because Wuhu Normal College had as little appeal for good students as it had for teachers, students, like teachers, were drawn from the barely qualified. Most of them, in fact, gave every evidence of owing their assignment to the school to peasant backgrounds and unassailable political records. Li Chi gathered, from sneering remarks made by his colleagues, that trying to teach Wuhu students anything, let alone art, would be a waste of time. His own observations tended to confirm this. He therefore did not waste either effort or emotion on trying to make artists out of his pupils. He knew how to talk to them so as to win their respect, and he reached an unspoken agreement with them. He passed them through his course with a minimum of friction as long as they made no demands on his time—or on the slender supply of art materials that was available for the class work. With a bit of luck, Li Chi thought that his circumstances might be molded into something idyllic.

The one obstacle to Li Chi's contentment in his new position was the fact that he was assigned to Comrade Ho's political discussion group. Comrade Ho was the Party Secretary of the so-called "cultural subjects section" of the faculty. This position, exalted though it sounded, was largely meaningless; what he really did was to lead a group of misfits and incompetents who nevertheless held Party or Youth League membership. He was a fat man with a prim little rosebud mouth. He walked slowly, his feet pointing out, and his arms swinging freely in imitation of Chairman Mao Tse-tung. He was barely literate, but he had the defensiveness, the pomposity, the shrewdness, and the vindictiveness of the ignorant. The members of his group were meant to maintain the illusion that their Party Secretary was a man of great wisdom and learning; retribution was swift and merciless on one who momentarily destroyed this illusion, but the rewards for preserving it were ample. He became a benevolent father image; he protected the individual from much of the outside harsh realities; and he created the impression among the members of his group that they were a little island of the cultural elite in a vast sea of intellectual mediocrity. After a few meetings it was impossible to avoid the feeling that Chairman Mao never made a decision without first checking it out with Comrade Ho.

To a realist like Li Chi, Comrade Ho and his group were a horror. Moreover, not being a Party or Youth League member, Li Chi by rights should not have been assigned to the group. At first, Comrade Ho was insulted at having a non-Party member thrust upon him; nevertheless, Li Chi's academic qualifications were so impressive that Comrade Ho's political superiority gave him a pleasant feeling of equality. He magnanimously set himself the task of teaching Li Chi all about Communism.

It was inevitable that Li Chi and Comrade Ho would find themselves in mortal conflict—their viewpoints were diametrically opposed—and their antagonism came into the open within three weeks of Li Chi's arrival.

The subject of discussion in Comrade Ho's group when Li Chi arrived was the contribution the college would make to the National Anniversary celebration in October. From on high, the instructions had come down that these contributions were to be extremely outstanding. They were to be called "sputniks," and they were to be the result of a phenomenal effort on the part of every citizen so that overnight China would be able to claim world leadership in every aspect of the arts and sciences. In this sort of competition, Ho's group of incompetents were hopeless, and it was Ho's genius that he could lead his followers in devising excuses that would save them from making any great effort, from outside criticism, and from any loss of self-respect or face. Thus Li Chi's offer to make an actual contribution was tactless. His fellow group members attacked him with scorn for having the arrogance to think his artistic talents were worthy of consideration by anyone. Ho shook his head sadly and talked ominously about the evil of "individualism."

Nevertheless, no one dared actually to prevent Li Chi from making a contribution. Everyone else outside Ho's group was doing something, and in fact hardly any classes were held while both students and faculty worked on their individual projects. Several of the science students, for example, had promised to construct an atom smasher twice as big as the ones that had been built in Europe and America; moreover, they were going to build it by using hand labor, enthusiasm, and love for the Party instead of tools, materials, equipment, parts, or even instructions on how to build such a machine

Li Chi's project was hardly in this class and was given no publicity, but it was at least capable of being finished. He offered to paint a picture using only paints he had made himself from local herbs. He would be putting to use the recipes he had learned from the old Hui woman in Lanchow. The picture he finally completed was a huge "heroic" canvas. Like his last watercolor in Peking, the new picture also was on the subject of the backyard furnace construction, the campaign for which had already begun. Li Chi chose this subject because he felt that Comrade Ho would try to prevent the painting from being exhibited. With the nationwide enthusiasm for backyard smelters at fever pitch, however, Li Chi did not believe that the Party Secretary would dare reject the painting.

Li Chi was wrong. Ho studied the picture scowling and with his little mouth puckered. Finally he confessed that he knew nothing about art but he did know something of politics. He felt that "political content" was lacking in the picture and that the backyard furnace campaign was much too serious and important to be given a wholly inadequate treatment in a work of art.

Nevertheless, he hastened to add that his opinion was worthless and that the matter would have to be "put before the masses," which is to say, his discussion group.

Once the group members understood Ho's opinion of the picture, they not only agreed fully (complimenting Ho on the brilliance of his critical faculty in art), but they attacked Li Chi for his artistic failure. Miss Sung, thin, intense, and passionately dedicated to exposing laxity in socialist discipline, accused Li Chi of coming to the meetings *filthy* (with paint all over him), and added, "I think Mr. Li Chi should *examine his conscience* to determine whether his failure is due as much to political backwardness as to a lack of talent."

The decision of the "masses" was that Li Chi should withdraw his project from the contributions to be made by the college to the National Anniversary; he was to confess his failure in a formal note addressed to the college authorities.

Li Chi wrote the letter as he had been ordered, but he worded it so as to imply that he had been overcome by an excess of modesty. He discussed the difficult problems he had had in making the dyes, and he expressed fear that the modern sophisticated people would think the ancient techniques uninteresting and unprogressive. At the time, Chairman Mao's "walking on two legs" principle was being introduced. The idea was that the ancient techniques were to be used with the modern wherever feasible so that progress could be made by any means available. Thus Li Chi's painting was a perfect example of the principle, and rejecting the painting would mean rejecting the principle. The college authorities demanded to see the painting. They promptly accepted it, brushing Li Chi's weak protests aside. Moreover, they announced that the college publicity concerning the National Anniversary "sputnik" contributions would center upon the painting.

Thus Comrade Ho and the others of his group lost face— badly. Comrade Ho's revenge came quickly, and it was cruel.

He arranged for Li Chi to be assigned to a team that worked a coal-grinding stone.

By now, the backyard furnace campaign of the Great Leap Forward was in full swing. Classes were again stopped—in fact, they had not really begun yet—while the whole nation labored to make China, virtually overnight, one of the world's leading industrial nations. The campaign was organized along military lines. The college became a division under the Wuhu general headquarters command. Each major department of the college became a regiment that was subdivided into battalions of seventy or eighty persons. The battalions were divided according to types of work. Li Chi and his group were assigned to a transportation battalion. It had three companies, one for horse carts (the horse carts, however, were drawn by human beings), another for handcarts, and another for shoulder carrying. Comrade Ho's group had the handcart company, but with some expert fumbling he managed to be left out completely in the short supply of carts. Therefore he assigned his "troops" temporarily to other units that seemed to be shorthanded. Thus his group members took care of electric lighting, carried messages, and repaired tools—all except Li Chi. Comrade Ho magnanimously gave him to the coal-grinding team, which had the most backbreaking job of all. Normally, animals were used to turn the great stone, and the human beings who worked it were exhausted after only a few minutes. Just as bad, they had to work in a dense cloud of coal dust. At night, these men would be too exhausted to bathe (the facilities were inadequate in any case); thus the coal dust was ground into their skin; their sheets and clothes became permanently stained with it, and before long their health would begin to suffer. The procedure was that only the strongest men were assigned to the coal grinders, and these men were rotated periodically so that one person did the heavy work for only a short period.

Whenever Li Chi's period was completed, however, Comrade

Ho immediately reassigned him to another of the grinding teams. At the same time, Comrade Ho was carefully spreading a few poisonous hints about Li Chi's past. Considering Li Chi's ideal class background and his high qualifications, Comrade Ho had no difficulty in putting across the idea that Li Chi must have committed a really horrible political crime to have been sentenced to the Wuhu Normal College and that he therefore should be regarded as political poison. Unquestionably, the college authorities were reconsidering their decision about Li Chi's painting. Li Chi himself would not be able to stand many more turns on the coal-grinding teams.

There is no telling what might have happened to Li Chi if fate had not intervened in an unsuspected and spectacular way. One day a group of reporters descended upon the college and demanded interviews with the "great new people's artist." In far-off Albania, Li Chi's picture "Red Smoke" had won a top prize in competition with artists from all the socialist fraternal countries.

Li Chi was brought at once to the office of the college president. He was, of course, filthy beyond description; he looked thin and exhausted, but he seemed to smile bravely through his suffering. It was now discovered how many tours of duty he had spent on the coal grinders. The reporters and college authorities were shocked. Li Chi had a superb chance for revenge; he had merely to state that Comrade Ho was responsible, and the man's brutal malice would be exposed. Li Chi took the opportunity for revenge on Comrade Ho, but in a more subtle manner. He claimed that he had volunteered for the hard work on the coal grinders. This had the effect of tripling the amount of publicity he received, and he became one of the national heroes of the backyard furnace campaign. Everyone in his discussion group received honor and attention simply because they were associated with Li Chi. The other group members knew that when Li Chi lied about volunteering for the coal-grinding teams, he had saved Comrade Ho from severe punishment. As a result the man was shamed before the group he led and, probably, made to feel ashamed of himself. Temporarily, at least, Comrade Ho was reduced to a pathetic little fat man whose only contribution to society was humility.

Li Chi's publicity had another aspect that affected his position in Wuhu. The fact was now revealed that he had not been in any trouble in Peking but had actually chosen Wuhu Normal College for his posting above all the other glamour positions that had been available to him. Thus Li Chi now became a special hero of the whole Anhwei Province, and in effect Wuhu Normal College basked in his reflected glory. For the first time in his life, Li Chi was exposed to a social life. The wife of the college president "took him in hand." She saw that he met the "right people." She confessed to a weakness for culture in general and artists in particular, and she began increasingly to seek his advice on matters of artistic taste or judgment.

One final aspect of the situation was novel and confusing to Li Chi. The prize for "Red Smoke" had included a sum of money that to Li Chi seemed astronomical. Never before, really, had he been aware of money as such. This is to say that he had lived his whole life at a point imperceptibly above the subsistence level; whether he had obtained the bare necessities in kind or through the purchasing power of money made little difference. He had never possessed the means to obtain goods and services that he did not need and that could be chosen purely on the basis of his pleasure.

At first, Li Chi's money sat in the bank, for the simple reason that he could think of nothing to do with it. The subject provided a means whereby Comrade Ho and the other group members sought to "let bygones be bygones," and attempted to put themselves back in Li Chi's good graces. They gave him endless advice about the money. Li Chi paid little attention to his fellow group members and even less attention to their advice. He now used the meetings to catch up on his sleep, and the others talked softly so as not to disturb him.

103

A week or two after his rise to fame in Wuhu, Li Chi made the first withdrawal of his prize money. It was for a good seat to witness the performance of a visiting opera company. At the performance he discovered one of the most effective of all means for disposing of large sums: a woman. He promptly fell in love with one of the singers, a girl named Miss Ling.

For the next few days, Li Chi sat in the front row for every show in which Miss Ling performed. Finally he worked up the courage to send her a flattering pastel drawing he had made of her. To his delight, she wrote back that she was much pleased at the attentions of a world-famous artist, and she invited him to meet her after the next performance.

Li Chi now began a whirlwind courtship of Miss Ling, and it quickly became the talk of Wuhu. The extraordinary aspect of this courtship was that it took place at the very height of the backyard furnace campaign when everyone except Party officials was working as much as sixteen hours a day. Li Chi was considered to have done his share in the excessive labor he had given to the coal-grinding stone. He therefore now held a post in a "logistics" battalion; his "company" was on emergency call to repair damaged or broken tools. The hours were not long, however; he had no classes to teach, and his companions in the "company" allowed him to leave if he were going to meet Miss Ling. The wife of the college president liked theatrical people as well as artists, and she invited Miss Ling and Li Chi together to her little parties. In fact, she tended to take charge of the romance.

Li Chi wanted very much to marry Miss Ling, and he proposed to her frequently. Apparently, she was more than willing to accept him, but he had one habit that bothered her, and made her hesitate. Whenever Li Chi felt the urge to paint a picture, he allowed himself to become so absorbed in the project that he not only forgot about everyone, including Miss Ling, he even neglected to eat and sleep adequately. At first, Miss Ling was hurt by Li Chi's sudden disappearances after days of ardent and

104

constant wooing. Then she became increasingly exasperated by his lapses.

Li Chi should have made a greater effort to change his ways. The president's wife warned him, and Li Chi himself should have seen from Miss Ling's attitude that he was risking one of the great loves of his life. Nevertheless, he seemed unable to help himself, and he neglected her for his art just once too often. When he finished his current painting, and re-entered society at large, he found that Miss Ling had married the business manager of her troupe.

Li Chi was genuinely heartbroken. His suffering was only too obvious and he won the sympathy of everyone who knew him. For a while he took to buying wine with which to console himself; he never lacked for friends who would help him drink the wine and give him heartfelt sympathy. He continued to sit every night in the first row of the theater and watch Miss Ling's performance. He grew steadily more pale and thin.

Suddenly one day, however, he seemed to have recovered completely not only his color but also his cheerful disposition. Within a few more days, it became only too obvious that Mrs. Szu, nee Miss Ling, had not been able to stand the nightly view of Li Chi's suffering, and had taken steps to relieve it. Before long, Wuhu was rocked by the scandal of Li Chi's affair with a married woman. The girl did announce that she intended to divorce her husband and marry Li Chi; she and her lover seemed helplessly lost in a storm of passion.

This was in early December, 1958. The backyard furnace campaign had come to an end on November 20th, and by then everyone except the top authorities knew that the whole Great Leap Forward was a failure. The full extent of the loss and damage to the nation, however, had not yet been determined; in the discussion-group meetings the slogan was "The concrete situation is infinitely encouraging." The officials were still bemused with optimism, and for the moment were tolerant of Li Chi's illicit love.

The trouble was that cause for optimism seldom lasted long in Communist China. In the winter of 1958, food shortages were a serious problem for the first time. In early January, 1959, therefore, the topic in the discussion groups was "Difficulties concerning the current market." The authorities were forced to use double-talk to explain why there should be hunger despite the announced huge increases in production.

The government also was losing face over Taiwan. During the previous August the threat to Taiwan had reached a climax, but the Americans had reacted with unexpected firmness and the Russians had unexpectedly refused to offer necessary equipment. The fact that Peking had had to retract in its position concerning Taiwan could no longer be hidden.

Hence the official good humor and leniency of early December, 1958, were lost by the middle of January, 1959. Two aspects of the loss affected Li Chi directly. One was a new movement called educational reform. It was an enlargement of the "red and expert" principle. Students in the schools and colleges were to get more political indoctrination. The institutions of learning were to become factories as well, and the factories were to become institutions of learning. Despite the increased time spent at labor and indoctrination, the pupils were to learn in a ten-year course what previously they had been given in twelve years. Finally, the emphasis was to be shifted even more to the "practical" studies, with unnecessary courses being eliminated. Art, of course, was strictly in the category of the unnecessary.

The other aspect concerned "Red Smoke" again. A high Peking official had stated that despite the prize given to the painting in a foreign country, the picture was in effect an insult to the Hui minority people; it seemed to indicate that the Hui thought only of rich food and comfort rather than of socialist construction. The wife of the college president suddenly stopped inviting Li Chi to her little parties.

Comrade Ho had made himself exquisitely sensitive to the

barometer of Li Chi's standing with the authorities. He knew the very moment when their leniency toward Li Chi's affair turned to impatience. Long before this, Comrade Ho had convinced himself that his original estimation of Li Chi—that Li Chi was a "backward element"—had been correct. He told himself, and then the skinny Miss Sung and his other favorites in the discussion group, that he had a duty to perform and that he must not let his foolish sentiment or generosity prevent him from carrying it out. "Leniency to the enemies of the people is cruelty to the people," he said.

Thus Li Chi's discussion group turned upon him suddenly After much harsh criticism—even insults—concerning his political backwardness, the accusations began to concentrate on his moral laxity. Miss Sung was the most indignant concerning Li Chi's "shocking and disgusting" relationship with a married woman. "I call upon Mr. Li Chi to deny that we should brand him as a degenerate and lascivious beast."

With growing anxiety, Li Chi perceived that a criminal case was being worked up against him. Under the extreme penalty of a declared "degenerate element," Comrade Ho might be able to obtain a severe sentence at "labor reform" for Li Chi, a sentence that would mean the end once and for all of Li Chi's career. Li Chi therefore decided upon a desperate means of defense. "I deny that I am a beast," he said in answer to Miss Sung's accusation. "Miss Ling and I love each other so deeply that we are unable to stay apart. Such love is unknown to animals, and it therefore is not bestial." He paused and then straightened. "Nevertheless, I have had an affair with a married woman. This is prohibited in our society. I demand, therefore, that you pass sentence upon me." He sat down amid an awkward silence.

Comrade Ho was shocked, and scowled fiercely to cover it. Li Chi's tactics suggested that he might still possess some hidden means of power. Ho suspected that Li Chi might well be bluffing. Nevertheless, the last time Ho had tried to punish Li Chi, he had failed and had himself suffered deep humiliation.

Moreover, what Ho really wanted was to have Li Chi dependent upon him. If Li Chi would confess, and throw himself on Ho's mercy, Ho could be lenient, magnanimous, and merciful—and he would have a hold over Li Chi that he would never give up. Conversely, Comrade Ho would gain nothing—and in fact might get in trouble—by trying to send Li Chi to labor reform. "We must not be hasty in this matter," he said finally. "We all should consider it carefully before taking action."

Li Chi had called Ho's bluff and was saved; everyone in the group knew that, for the moment at least, Comrade Ho lacked the courage for further attack. Furthermore, only a week later "Red Smoke" was again in the news. Li Chi deduced that the picture had become caught in the Sino-Soviet conflict, which by now was being gossiped about openly. Apparently the Peking authorities had mistakenly believed that originally the Russian art critics had favored "Red Smoke"; for this reason, Peking had rejected the picture; now, however, it was learned that the Albanian—not the Russian—critics had given the picture the prize. Hence Li Chi's painting once more was "a superb example of socialist realism, illustrating the fraternal love that exists between the Han and the minority peoples."

Once more, Comrade Ho and the other group members became deeply respectful, and Li Chi was able to sleep again through the meetings. The president's wife, however, advised him seriously that he should stop his affair with the opera singer. He took the advice because he did not want to endanger the girl's position. Before long, the girl's troupe left Wuhu, and the scandal was soon forgotten.

Li Chi, however, was no longer happy at the college. The intrigues and the backbiting, while not so bad as in Peking, were enough to exasperate him. He began to feel the longing once more for the rural areas and the peasant folk he understood.

Oddly enough, the chances of his getting to the countryside should have been good. The communes had been organized the previous autumn, and by February, 1959, the down-to-the-countryside (*hsia fang*) movement was launched. A large group from the Normal College was expected to "volunteer" for labor at a commune, but Comrade Ho was adroit in keeping himself and his group off the list. Li Chi would have volunteered, but he was afraid of a refusal that would make it impossible for him ever to get to a commune.

Help in his predicament came from an unexpected quarter and under surprising circumstances. He really had loved Miss Ling, and giving her up had been hard. Because of this he experienced what an older and wiser man might have avoided: he was caught on the rebound. A small troupe of singers and dancers moved in to replace the opera group. One of the dancing girls, apparently, was attracted by Li Chi's ugly charm, and almost at once he found himself having an affair with her. To protect her, he was as discreet as possible; he would not see her either at the theater or at the dormitory where she lived with the other members of the troupe under the watchful eye of a young but stern Party Secretary. It was spring now, and he therefore was able to meet her outside. Their favorite trysting place was an open potato field next to the building where her troupe was quartered. In the middle of this field was a large stone bin in which potatoes were stored. The shadow of this bin offered a reasonable amount of privacy.

One day, whoever was in charge of the field discovered that potatoes that were still stored in the bin were being stolen. Thus a guard was placed on the bin. Li Chi and his new love did not know this, and they did not see the guard as they made their way quietly that night to the bin. The guard heard them, of course, and assumed that they were the thieves. Because he was only one to their two, he did not accost them, but instead went to the building nearby for help.

The Party Secretary in charge of the troupe had the most authority. He quickly called out his troupe and had them surround the field. Then the group began to close in around the bin.

Fortunately, Li Chi and his love heard people approaching in time to make themselves presentable. Suddenly they were spotted. Li Chi and the dancing girl were seized roughly. When the lantern was brought, the Party Secretary assumed that the dancing girl had been seized in error; that is to say, that she had come out with the others and had been part of the ring. The girl did not argue the matter, nor did Li Chi give her away.

That left Li Chi, however, as the thief. He racked his brains for some explanation that would free him from this predicament. Suddenly he saw the woman who was standing next to the Party Secretary. She recognized him at the same moment, and turned to hide her face. But it was too late. Li Chi called her name, and the wife of the college president turned back to him; her red face and downcast eyes indicated only too clearly why she was here with the young Party Secretary at one in the morning. Li Chi looked at her questioningly.

"This isn't the thief," she said to the Party Secretary. "You'd better have him released and apologize to him—"

Li Chi smiled at the president's wife, a smile that he hoped would assure her that her little secret was safe with him—as long as his little secret was safe with her.

It seems quite clear, however, that the president's wife did not feel entirely secure with Li Chi so near. Only the next day, the president announced that the college *hsia fang* group had been changed. The new enrollment included the whole of Comrade Ho's group.

CHAPTER IX

The Production Team

When Li Chi arrived at the commune, a feeling of great joy and peace descended upon him. In the small village that contained the production brigade headquarters, he was given a room in the hut of an old peasant couple. He shared the room with the couple's two unmarried sons, one of whom was the leader of the production team on which Li Chi would work.

He perceived at once that these simple peasants had expected to be much in awe of a highly educated professor from the city. Thus they were happily surprised to find that he too was at heart an Anhwei peasant and that his education had been the result of good fortune. They were proud of him, and they wanted to like him.

To like him, however, they would have to trust him. Before that first evening was over, Li Chi knew that he wanted the friendship of these kindly people more than he had ever wanted anything else. He also knew that winning their trust would be the most difficult task he had ever attempted. Worst, he was aware that, if he were successful, he might well defeat the whole purpose of the effort because he would bring upon himself the extreme enmity of the local officials. The reason for this dilemma concerned the truth as opposed to the Communist pretenses concerning the whole commune experiment. The Peking leaders maintained that the experiment was begun because of an irresistible demand from the rural masses for "advanced cooperativization," that the peasants accepted commune living happily, and that the communes were miraculously successful in raising the peasant living standard.

None of this, of course, was true. From the beginning the peasants had resisted with varying degrees of intensity the regime's whole policy of ever-expanded cooperativization, and they had had to be coerced into accepting the communes. Generally, they had objected to commune living strenuously enough so that in most places this aspect of the experiment was abandoned; in fact the communes represented nothing more than increased concentration of property ownership; in other words, the property of several comparatively small farm cooperatives (now called production brigades) had been combined into one large unit, a commune, which was being touted as a "revolutionary new concept in socioeconomic science" and as "concrete evidence of Mao Tse-tung's creative genius."

And finally the communes had brought about no rise in the peasant living standard. In fact, the standard had been lowered in many areas. In the first place, the peasants simply did not work as hard for "socialist construction" as they did for themselves, so that agricultural production decreased. Again, their labor was frequently employed inefficiently; often, for example, they were set to digging irrigation ditches when they should have been planting, or they might be made to plant rice where only potatoes could be grown. Furthermore, the authorities had taken arbitrarily most of the agricultural profits to pay the tremendous cost of the Great Leap. And finally, sheer administrative inefficiency was sure to prevent the communes from making a good showing; a commune was a vast and complicated enterprise that required well-trained administrators. The number of trained men was wholly inadequate; there were not even enough simple bookkeepers to ensure that some kind of equitable distribution of the commune's produce would be made.

The result of all this was varying degrees of near chaos throughout the mainland's rural areas. In most places, the peasants were demoralized. In Li Chi's village, the people after giving up their possessions and having worked for an entire year found that their earnings from the commune amounted to slightly less than four yuan per worker. They were shocked, disillusioned, angry, and sullen. In disgust, some of the younger men ran away to the cities in hope of finding better paid industrial jobs. Those who stayed were even less inclined to work hard than before; in fact, on a few occasions they had had to be dragged forcibly into the fields.

These were the circumstances into which the *hsia fang* group were introduced. The official pretense was that the *hsia fang* was a spontaneous movement on the part of the urban population to participate in the glorious cooperativization program. The truth was, of course, that those who were "sent down to the countryside" had no choice in the matter. Apparently, the Party planners believed that the extra labor would help ensure increased agricultural productivity and also forestall widespread urban unemployment that the failure of the Great Leap was already bringing about. Moreover, the punitive nature of the movement, while never admitted openly, was unmistakable; those who had "bloomed" unacceptably during the Hundred Flowers or who were declared to need "ideological remolding" were the first to be sent, and their proper behavior was demanded on the threat of being made to spend additional months—or years—as farm laborers.

In the communes themselves, however, the authorities maintained all the official pretenses but obviously had a completely different attitude toward the *hsia fang*. The commune cadres may have spared their superiors the truth about the demoralization of the peasants, but they themselves must have been aware of the resentment against them smoldering under the surface. Generally, therefore, they wanted the *hsia fang* to perform a propaganda function with the peasants, to persuade the peasants that the commune experiment was a great success nationally (even if it was a failure locally) and that the Party cadres were noble, infallible, and virtuous. To perform this propaganda function, the *hsia fang* were pressed constantly to "overcome the barrier of the masses"; this meant overcoming the urban dweller's instinctive distaste for his seemingly boorish country cousin, at least to the extent of being able to communicate with him.

But no more than that—what the commune cadres feared the most was that the peasants would disaffect the *hsia fang* and thereby enable the rural and urban groups to unite in opposition to the regime. Thus even a hint that one of the *hsia fang* was becoming really friendly with and sympathetic to the peasants would bring about instant retribution from the authorities for the vague but serious crime of "unprincipled in dealing with the masses."

This was the danger that Li Chi incurred in dealing with the peasant family. Out of Comrade Ho's group, he was the only one quartered with the "masses." This was partly because he was the only one of the group who was not a Youth League or Party member and partly because, having come originally from the peasants, he could be expected to understand them. Not for a minute, however, did the authorities believe that Li Chi would identify himself and sympathize with the peasants. According to the dogma, a man's behavior was unalterably fixed according to his class or social stratum. Li Chi was now an urban intellectual, and regardless of what he might have been once, the cadres believed that he would act only in accordance with the self-interest of the urban intellectual. The fact that Li Chi could be an artist, a university graduate, a city dweller, and at the same time prefer country living and country people contradicted dogma and was thus unbelievable. This belief was the one advantage Li Chi had in his design for winning the friendship of the peasant family.

Li Chi began methodically to recast the image Comrade Ho's group had of him. At the commune, the *hsia fang* worked only six hours a day in the fields; they spent *four hours a day* in political discussion meetings. The first meetings were on the subject "The Importance of Thought Reform." Each member was made to write a report on his past errors in political thinking. The idea was to blacken himself as much as possible so that later, at the end of the *hsia fang* term, he could claim that the experience had benefited him; the greater the contrast between "before" and "after," the more praise would be implied to the whole "down to the countryside" movement.

Having described how evil he had been, each group member next outlined in his report the means whereby he would overcome the deficiencies. He would "give his whole heart to the Party and to Chairman Mao." He would become a "willing tool of the Party" and be prepared to "dedicate his all to the Party." He would cultivate even greater enthusiasm for collectivism, for the "noble cause of Communism," and for the leadership of the Party. If he came from bourgeois origins—as did most of the group members—he would repudiate the "ugly class nature" of his background, and he would strive to overcome the "barrier of the masses" and the "barrier of the living standard."

Finally, he described what improvements in his character he expected to achieve as a result of his *hsia fang* experience; he would have put behind him forever "disregard of organization and of discipline in daily living." He would have acquired a heightened awareness of the benefits of collectivization and the joy that comes from giving labor without thought of reward. And, of course, he would have learned a new regard for the Party and its glorious leaders.

Li Chi's report did not follow the customary outline. He admitted that he had made some mistakes in his past, but "who has not?" he asked. Most of his mistakes, however, could be blamed on the Party, which had taken him from the countryside in the erroneous belief that it could make an artist and an intellectual of him. Now the Party seemed to be trying to remedy its errors concerning him and had sent him back where he belonged. He was happy and he did not need to overcome the "barrier of the masses" because he was already one of the masses; similarly, he did not need to overcome the "living standard barrier" because the living standard at the commune was no worse than what he had endured as a child. As for the commune "experiment," how could anyone praise it and the Party until the success of the experiment had been determined beyond all doubt? He ended by saying that he himself intended to give the experiment the "benefit of the doubt" and to work hard to make it a success.

The report shocked and infuriated Comrade Ho. He unleashed the other group members at Li Chi. The trouble was, however, that nothing in the report could be used against him. The report reflected an attitude that, according to the official *pretense,* was perfectly logical and acceptable. Comrade Ho, in desperation, showed Li Chi's report to one of the higher Party functionaries from the college. This man also was angered, and he went so far as to direct two of Comrade Ho's group meetings in order to castigate Li Chi.

Even he, however, could do no more than talk vaguely of "individualism" and of "failure to give one's heart to the Party." Moreover, because *hsia fang* was in itself considered a kind of punishment, the authorities could do little about Li Chi. Thus they soon dropped the subject, having done no more than make threats to the effect that, as a "backward element," Li Chi might have to stay indefinitely at the commune

Nevertheless, as Li Chi had well known, the subject of his unorthodox report became gossip among the peasants. The peasants were delighted with the story. They began to see Li Chi as one of themselves who, in addition, had the cleverness and the courage to take advantage of the hated cadres. Cautiously, the other members of his production team began to ask his advice on how to deal with the authorities. The advice Li Chi gave was always good; it always benefited the peasants at the expense of the cadres, and it reflected his greater knowledge of the strength and weaknesses of the authorities.

At the same time, the cadres were fully aware of Li Chi's developing relationship with the peasants and the effects it could have. The cadres could be expected to respond in a decisive manner, and it was now that the peasants were able to help Li Chi.

Their help took advantage of the authorities' practice of giving emulation prizes. To encourage greater effort, the authorities tried hard to instill a spirit of competition between the peasant workers; in almost every aspect of the commune's activity, prizes were given to those whose production was highest or whose effort had been the greatest. The prizes were insignificant—a few cigarettes, perhaps, or an extra handful of rice—but they were accompanied by much publicity and loud praise. Unknown to the authorities, the peasants treated the emulation drive as a joke, and invariably the winner was arranged by them in advance. When they had decided who the winner would be, other peasants simply saw to it that the winner was credited with part of their own work. Sometimes, for example, it amused the peasants to have the weakest, scrawniest little man in the brigade credited with fantastic feats of strength. Thus when Li Chi was in danger from the authorities for helping the peasants, he suddenly found that he was winning practically all the prizes. He pulled the most weeds, planted the most seeds, cultivated the longest rows, carried the most manure, irrigated the largest plots, and so on. News of his achievements went all the way back to Wuhu, and once again the authorities there basked in his reflected glory.

Under these circumstances, the authorities at the commune could hardly attack the man who was the hero of both the commune and the *hsia fang* group. In this situation, Comrade Ho had the most difficulty. As usual, he had been highly successful in avoiding work for himself and for the other members of his group. As a result of Li Chi's achievement, the record of the others appeared even worse than it was. The others no longer bothered to hide their hatred of Li Chi, and their attacks on him became almost constant.

At the same time, they had to be cautious. Thus, for example, a charge of "he puts himself in opposition to the Party" could hardly be valid when other and higher Party members were praising him extravagantly. An attempt was made to "struggle" against him for failure to confess to shortcomings the manual labor of *hsia fang* was intended to overcome. Li Chi's reply was: "I have nothing whatever to criticize myself for. I do not have any incorrect thinking about this countryside experience. I did not ask to be made an artist and a teacher. I'm a peasant, and this is where I belong—where I *want* to be. I like what I'm doing. I'm happy here, and I do not need the Party to tell me that I *should* be happy here."

Comrade Ho forgot himself to the extent of calling Li Chi a liar. He said that what Li Chi really liked was the soft life of an intellectual, with nothing to do but daub paint, eat rich food, and enjoy the luxuries of the city.

To this, Li Chi merely laughed. "If that's what you think," he said, "leave me here forever. You won't hear any complaints from me."

Comrade Ho was forced to drop the matter, but he soon returned to the attack. The subject then was the "hardships of living in the commune." The discomforts and shortages, especially of food, were expected to cause much distress among the *hsia fang* people. The Party's line was that the hardship was only in the mind and was the result of incorrect thinking; with the right thinking the so-called hardship could be surmounted. Thus, Li Chi was asked first how he managed to overcome the hardship of commune living; by admitting only that commune living was a hardship, he would be guilty of incorrect thinking and therefore could be accused of needing thought reform.

Li Chi, however, easily avoided this trap even if he had no way of knowing the Party line in advance. "What hardship?" he asked innocently. "I feel no discomfort here. This is the living standard in which I was raised. I have no complaints and I don't need the Party to tell me how to endure this life. If you Communists, instead of talking all the time, would get out in the fields and work as we peasants do, you wouldn't have time to think so much about 'hardship.' "

Comrade Ho could only sputter and pound his table with frustration and rage.

Finally, in desperation, Li Chi's affair with the married woman, the opera singer, was revived. He was called all the usual bad names and was accused once more of being a degenerate and lecherous beast. This time, however, it was pointed out that despite the heinousness of Li Chi's crimes, the Party had been patient, sympathetic, and merciful; he therefore owed the Party gratitude.

Li Chi, however, refused even this bait. "I accuse the Party of laxity," he said. "I was wrong to have had an affair with a married woman. I stated that I deserved to be punished, and I demanded that the Party deal with my case in accordance with the people's justice. Why was no action taken?"

Once again, Comrade Ho was forced to retreat, sputtering in rage and frustration. He reported the problem of Li Chi to his superiors who sat in on Ho's meetings. They, too, saw that, in effect, Li Chi was making fun of the whole regime; he was holding it up to ridicule to the masses. Nevertheless, the cadres could do nothing to him without abandoning the whole façade of pretenses.

The Communists' basic claim was that their unquestioned leadership and their indoctrination were necessary if the working classes were to develop the correct progressive attitude toward labor and toward self-improvement that would enable the worker to rise above his environment and contribute toward a worker's paradise. Li Chi came from the ideal background and he had "improved" himself so that he had risen to high intellectual status. In addition, he had the proper attitude toward manual labor and he had a genuine identification with the masses, with whom, in fact, he obviously was popular. In short, he was the perfect "Communist man."

This is to say, he would have been if he would only admit that his perfection and his achievements were the result of the benefits of Communist-socialism and the Party. Li Chi categorically refused to do this. He insisted that the Party had given him nothing; it had only used him. He was what he was *in spite of* —not because of—the Party. This attitude made the Communists who dealt with him feel that their leadership was unnecessary, that their authority was unjustly imposed, and that their political power was arbitrarily retained for the sake of the power itself. This feeling tore at the very foundation of a Communist's sense of security. If *he* could be made to see that his power could not be rationalized and therefore was tyranny, what must the masses really think of the regime?

What the peasant masses felt about the regime varied widely from area to area, and even from person to person. What every peasant disliked the most about the regime, however, was the Communist practice of dividing the peasants against each other. Nowhere was this practice more evident than in the quota and work-point system that was enforced in the communes.

This system began with "target" production figures determined by the top authorities for the whole commune. The quantity of these targets then was divided among the various brigades. An attempt was made to equalize the quotas by assigning smaller quotas to brigades with poorer land.

When the brigade had its quota, the heads of its production teams were called together. The yield-per-*mou* for every piece of land was estimated at a figure so that the total would achieve or surpass the quota. No two pieces of land had the same qualitative or quantitative productivity. Pressure was put on each team leader to promise to produce as high as possible a percentage of the brigade's quota. On the other hand, the team's return depended upon achieving the production promised, otherwise penalties were enforced. Hence the team leaders were forced to struggle against each other to obtain the lowest possible quota, in relation to the others.

To make this system even worse, the quotas established for each brigade were literally ten or more times as high as the land was capable of producing under any circumstances. Thus the teams fought for quota assignments the lowest of which were utterly impossible to achieve. When the team leaders asked how their land could be expected to produce ten times the quantity it ever had before, they were told that "deep plowing and close planting" were the answers. Comrade Mao Tse-tung himself had assured the nation that this was so. Thus no one dared to deny it, and the poor peasants on the production team were stuck with the responsibility for the blunders of others.

Some teams refused to plant the extra seed, knowing that "close planting" would result in lower, rather than higher, productivity. In these cases, their fields were taken temporarily out of their jurisdiction and were close-planted by other workers. Other teams, in a kind of resistance, did precisely what they were told to do, knowing that the result would prove the authorities wrong. The attitude of the whole peasant class was such that adequate production was impossible and that worse food shortages in the future were inevitable.

Li Chi's fellow team members also were demoralized when their leader returned to them from the brigade meeting with an absurdly high quota assignment for the season. Li Chi, however, now saw his chance to win the trust and friendship of his team members once for all.

He pointed out to them, first, that the quota figures were too ridiculous to have any real significance. They would be used for propaganda purposes outside, but in the commune the teams that produced the largest amount of actual crops would win the greatest rewards. Li Chi added that almost without exception the attitude of the members of the other teams was to do as little work as possible. Thus Li Chi's team had a good chance to come out on top. His suggestion was that the extra seed for close planting should be drawn with all the appropriate praise for the genius of Chairman Mao. Instead of planting the extra seed, however, it should be divided among the team members as a sort of secret bonus, "to the masses from the Party," and used for a feast on some notable occasion. Thereupon, their land plot should be planted, cultivated, and worked to get the highest possible yield.

The men laughed with delight. "With very little effort," the leader said, "we'll produce more than anyone else. The cadres will have to give us a reasonable share of the harvest."

But Li Chi shook his head. "No one will get a reasonable share of the harvest," he said. "There will hardly be enough to go around, and they can't afford to let any large numbers of us starve. Thus no one will be given more than the absolute minimum, even if none of us draws any less." He looked around to make sure that no cadre was within hearing distance. "What we should do," he said in a lower voice, "is produce as much as we can, but declare only as much as the others do—a little bit more than the average. What we have left will be our reward for clearer foresight."

Again the men laughed. Nothing delighted them more than a good trick to play on the cadres.

Thus in the autumn of 1959, Li Chi and his team mates were able to set aside and hide a sizable portion of their harvest yield. That winter he and his friends suffered little from the drastic food shortage. The fact that they had enough food was only too apparent; they showed no signs of malnutrition and they had more energy than the others, even in the cold weather. The authorities, therefore, suspected something of what had been done. The team leader was thoroughly investigated, not once, but several times. Each time, however, the team members stood staunchly behind their leader, and Li Chi briefed them all on how to answer the cadres' questions. Moreover, the authorities had praised Li Chi's team highly as one of the ten that had achieved the highest productivity. Thus the investigation was finally dropped.

Li Chi settled down happily to a new life. He had the admiration and friendship of people he loved, and for the present at least, although Comrade Ho and the commune authorities hated him, they were forced to leave him alone.

CHAPTER X

The People's Artist

In July and August of 1960, Li Chi and his superior at the college, Mr. Wei, were called upon to leave the commune temporarily in order to attend the Third Congress of Chinese Writers and Artists in Peking. They were put in charge of four other men from the commune who also had been invited to the Congress. These other four were peasants who, without any training, had shown a natural talent for painting; thus, they were true examples of the "people's artists" and of the country's Great Leap Forward in culture.

To Mr. Wei and the four peasants, the trip promised to be the most exciting experience of their lives, and they anticipated it with mingled rapture and terror. They practically clung to Li Chi; to them he was a man of the world of the most seasoned variety, and they depended upon him to guide them, to protect them from the unknown hazards of the Big City, and to show them the wonders of urban civilization. Li Chi was patient and sympathetic with his charges, and he developed for them the protectiveness of a mother hen.

Unfortunately, however, until they reached Peking, Li Chi did not bother to look at the pictures each of the peasants had painted and were to exhibit at the Congress. The quality of the paintings could be said to "turn back the clock" of the people's art for a number of decades. Three of the pictures, Li Chi thought, could be hidden in a distant, carefully unlit corner of the exhibition galleries. It was the fourth painting, however, that made both Li Chi and Mr. Wei gasp with horror.

The picture showed a line of about a dozen gaunt men, dressed in filthy rags, carrying buckets from latrines in the background. By itself, this might make the picture passable as an illustration of the fertilizer campaign. The title, however, in large, glaring, indelible characters, read: "World-famous Artists and Writers Carry Shit at Our Commune."

On second look, Li Chi decided that the picture, despite the crudity of its execution, was not entirely without merit; at least the faces of the people were immediately recognizable. They were indeed some of the country's most famous artists. In fact, six or seven years previously, at the Second Congress of Chinese Artists and Writers, all these men had been among the most prominent delegates. At the first Hundred Flowers campaign in the spring of 1957, however, they had "bloomed" indiscreetly. Having been declared "rightist-thinking persons"—a somewhat lesser crime than outright "rightists"—they had been sentenced to long-term *hsia fang* instead of to the dreaded "labor reform."

What made the picture so shocking, however, was the grossness of its insult to the regime. Any artist or writer—in fact, any intellectual—who looked at that picture was shown graphically what the Communist authorities really thought of culture. Even worse, the picture seemed to say: "This is where the real intellectuals in a Communist society belong; of what groveling compromises, what cowardly betrayals are *you* guilty that you are not here with us?"

A final extraordinary aspect of the picture was that Lo Fu,

the painter of it, saw none of the social and political commentary in his work. He was not surprised that famous people would come to work on the land; he was flattered that they came to his part of the country, but he could not imagine that they were demeaned by being there. In his simplicity, he saw nothing degrading in their carrying the night soil from the latrines to the fields; he himself had done it often, and he did not feel degraded. These people had treated him well; they had exposed him to the pleasure of painting; he liked them, and in gratitude he had depicted them precisely as he saw them. Finally, to him, his title was not crude; his peasant directness made him avoid elegant euphemisms, and he labeled his work in the terse terms that he felt were the most descriptive. It was simply impossible to explain to him what was wrong with his painting.

Mr. Wei drew Li Chi aside. "What shall we do?" the older man asked, wringing his hands. "We can't let that picture be seen. We can't even let Lo Fu register for the Congress."

"His heart will be broken," Li Chi said.

"Better his heart than his skull," Wei said. "Any intellectual who sees that picture will think that it was done by a counter-revolutionary."

"But the cadres are not intellectuals," Li Chi said. He had found, suddenly, that he wanted very much to exhibit Lo Fu's painting. This was only partly because he did not want to disappoint the simple and trusting peasant; it was also because he wanted the other artists to face the truth about their position in this society, and the future they could expect if they attempted to develop the individualism and integrity that were necessary to art of any real value.

Thus, to Mr. Wei's horror, Li Chi suddenly said that the picture would be entered and exhibited. "The trick is to feature the picture, not hide it," Li Chi said, "and I must be sure to take the responsibility for it."

Li Chi was one of the group that had been made responsible for the exhibition of the works of the "people's artists." His old associates at the Art Institute were in charge of most aspects of the graphic arts part of the Congress, and because currently his painting "Red Smoke" was approved, he too was socially and professionally well regarded. Thus he was able to arrange for Lo Fu's picture to be prominently displayed; in fact, he had it put on an easel and placed in the middle of the floor of the main exhibition hall.

As he expected, the picture stayed on exhibition for less than two hours. Soon after its sudden disappearance, Li Chi was notified by a frozen-faced cadre that his presence was expected at an emergency meeting. The meeting was held by the Institute's head art critic and expert, the old man who had been forced to change his opinion so often about "Red Smoke." He was backed by three ranking Party Secretaries whose outrage was only too obvious. The audience included the Art Institute group with which Li Chi was working, the four peasants he had brought from the commune, and the terrified Mr. Wei. Li Chi smiled reassuringly at Lo Fu.

"We are here," the old art critic began, "to consider the merits—or otherwise—of a so-called painting entitled—ahem—the painting you see before you. I demand to know who is responsible for this—this whatever you call it—"

"Sir, I am happy and proud to claim that honor," Li Chi said, jumping to his feet. He beamed at the critic and the Party Secretaries. "And I can well understand your loss of words when confronted with this masterpiece of the people's art."

"Masterpiece!" the old critic exclaimed. "Why, you ignorant, incompetent, artistic *criminal*—"

"Indeed, sir," Li Chi said calmly, "that is precisely what I was —an ignorant artistic criminal when I first looked at that painting and failed to appreciate the important political message it contained."

"Now see here, young man," the critic began, but one of the Party Secretaries interrupted him.

"What message?" the Communist demanded, and the menace in his voice was unmistakable.

"Why, simply the message that just happens to be the theme

of this Congress, that's all," Li Chi said. "And not only that, the message which is contained in the artistic method of the master artist of us all, our glorious leader, Chairman Mao."

The Party Secretary was unimpressed. "What's the message?" he demanded again, and the menace in his voice was even more distinct.

" 'Combining of revolutionary realism and revolutionary romanticism in the effort to depict the glory of our heroic epoch,' " Li Chi quoted.

"You call that—that vulgarism, that *abomination*—the 'glory of our heroic epoch'?" the critic demanded. His voice shook with indignation.

"Vulgar and abominable—the very two words I used myself, sir, when I first saw that picture," Li Chi said. "But then I realized how wrong I was, how arrogantly aloof from the masses my artistic judgment had become. Only when I threw off the degenerate bourgeois concept of art, and studied this picture in its true proletarian aspects did I come to perceive and appreciate its glorious message."

The critic looked confused, and he turned questioningly to the Party Secretaries.

"All right," one of the secretaries said, "carrying shit is proletarian art. But those turtles in that picture are rightists. One death is too good for them."

"Ah, no," Li Chi said reprovingly. " 'Cure the disease and save the patient,' and as Chairman Mao also told us, such people are to be re-educated to serve socialist construction. The people in this picture *are* serving, and from the masses, our direct-thinking people's artist is the first one to perceive it. Would you belittle the contribution the people in this picture are making just because they are *famous* people?"

At this point, even the Party Secretaries hesitated in confusion, and Li Chi therefore pushed on to make his point. "Chairman Mao and all the great Party leaders have told us of the glorious tomorrow for which we work today, a tomorrow in which the simplest laborer will be an artist and the greatest artist a laborer. All of it is perfectly expressed in this one painting. Here is Lo Fu, a simple laborer; he as an artist has painted a picture of great artists doing simple labor. Can you think of any better way of expressing the whole of our socialist construction effort?"

A murmur went through the audience, and everyone leaned forward to look at the picture again, this time more closely.

"May I recall for you that magic formula given by our brilliant leaders to artists and writers? A work of art must reflect accurately the particular era in which it was created and also, in addition, it must promote or stimulate the progress—the Leap Forward—into the socialist era. Here in this picture is the perfect expression of the formula. The very fact that it was painted by a simple laborer demonstrates the cultural Leap Forward, and the subject of the painting indicates that all the elements of our society are contributing to socialist construction. I am in awe of the power of the masses and of the sheer brilliance with which a simple people's artist is able to say so effectively with an untutored brush—"

The critic and the Party Secretaries held a consultation. "Upon closer scrutiny of this picture," the old critic said finally, "one cannot overlook certain political overtones that tend rather to be enhanced and harmonized by the somewhat primitive technique—"

Li Chi interrupted the old man. "Can you not say that this picture is a brilliant and outstanding example of the people's art in a socialist culture?" he demanded to know.

". . . uh, such an evaluation would not be without some certain validity," the old man said nervously.

The painting was put back in its place of prominence and was seen by most of the delegates. The Party Secretaries of the Art Institute were responsible for it now. Inevitably, someone higher up objected to it; arguments about its political content— if any—were apparently frequent and caustic, but the painting remained on exhibition during the rest of the time that Li Chi and his companions spent in Peking. Lo Fu understood little of the controversy about his picture; he knew only that Li Chi had helped him win much flattering praise. He was infinitely grateful, and Li Chi won the undying friendship of Lo Fu and the other three peasant artists.

Later that year this friendship proved invaluable to Li Chi. The food shortage was particularly bad from November of 1960 into January of 1961. Malnutrition diseases were widespread, work had to be curtailed, and even the political discussion meetings were temporarily eliminated. Because fertilizer and seed had been in meager supply, Li Chi and the other members of his production team had not been able to hold out part of their harvest as they had done previously. Finally, Li Chi spent the last of his prize money from "Red Smoke" on buying food. Nevertheless, most of the peasants had anticipated the food shortage and had managed to put aside a little something. Lo Fu desired frequently to reminisce with Li Chi about their Peking trip, and he always brought a small amount of food of some kind whenever he visited Li Chi. Thus, although Li Chi spent most of his days that winter playing cards to keep his mind off his hunger, he managed to get through the period without any serious difficulty.

CHAPTER XI

The Locomotive

In early 1961, the food shortage was alleviated slightly. By the time the weather had softened sufficiently to promise spring, the morale of the Chinese people began to rise. Hope was reborn, and in discussion-group meetings, the voice of Communism could be heard throughout the land, cooing, "The current concrete situation is infinitely promising."

Li Chi, however, found the refrain infinitely depressing. Life had begun to stir within him again, and he felt that he simply could not endure the endless, deadly dull discussion-group meetings ahead. An important reason for this restlessness concerned Miss Fei. She was really Mrs. Hsia now, but Li Chi remembered her as she was before she married, the beautiful tragic girl from the bourgeoisie who had been the first great love in his life.

After she had been expelled from the Art Institute, Li Chi had acquired the habit of writing to her periodically. Her replies were friendly even if they were not very personal, and they had continued even after she married Hsia the engineer.

Recently, however, Hsia had managed to get himself put on the "honor roll" of his group, and had been granted the glorious privilege of contributing to socialist construction through manual labor in a frontier district. Fortunately, Miss Fei herself had not been given similar honor. Reading between the lines of her letters, Li Chi gathered that the authorities harassed her almost constantly because of her class background but that otherwise her position was fairly secure. She had a job painting designs on pottery that was used for the export trade, and although she hated the work she was apparently so good at it that she was in no danger of losing the job. The work did not occupy all her time, however, and after her husband had left, Miss Fei had begun to take the initiative in writing to Li Chi; since then her letters had become increasingly frequent, personal and warm. As a result, Li Chi's feeling of rebirth in the spring of 1961 was accompanied by an urgent desire to visit Miss Fei.

The likelihood of an opportunity for such a visit, however, seemed nil. In the first place the woman lived an expensive two-day journey to the South by boat and train, and Li Chi had no money for the fare. Moreover, since the Great Leap the nation's transportation capacity had been seriously reduced so that only essential travel was permitted. This meant that an official authorization for his trip would require him to be assigned to a project of practically national importance sponsored by a high officer.

In the second place, Comrade Ho would take great pleasure in prohibiting the trip if he even suspected that, for any reason whatever, Li Chi *desired* it. Furthermore, during the January political discussion meetings in which the group summarized each member's commune experience, the unanimous conclusion of Li Chi's group had been that he had learned nothing from the experience and that he was basically an unregenerate "backward element" who stood in need of vigorous political self-reform. Who would offer such a person relief from the soul-cleansing rigors of the commune with a pleasant all-expense trip to the South?

One day, however, Li Chi's eye was caught by newspaper pictures of a railway engineer whom the authorities were publicizing in behalf of an official campaign called "Love Your Locomotive." The campaign, apparently, was meant to inspire railway workers to donate more time and effort to the maintenance and repair of the overworked equipment. This matter, of course, had nothing to do with Li Chi, and he gave it his attention only because he saw that the model engineer happened to come from the same city in which Miss Fei lived.

Li Chi studied the pictures carefully. He perceived at once that the photographs were inexpertly taken. They lacked clarity, and the impression they gave was not what obviously was intended. The railway equipment looked so shabby that one could not believe it had been given exceptional care by the model engineer. The engineer himself was young and handsome, but he was posed so stiffly and self-consciously that one doubted his alleged love for his engine. In fact his dental grin was so obviously fake that one had the impression he secretly loathed the mechanical beast and was inclined to kick it when no one was looking.

After considerable thought, Li Chi addressed a letter to the commune's director of propaganda. In the letter, Li Chi revealed a deep sympathy for the government's transportation problem, great admiration for the "Love Your Locomotive" campaign, and an intense desire to contribute to it. Thereupon, he described glowingly a picture he wanted to paint. It would depict a glossy, ultramodern, superpowerful locomotive, symbolizing China's magnificent industrialization and socialist construction program under the inspired leadership of the glorious Communist Party and the beloved Chairman Mao. The locomotive would be shown moving at headlong, irresistible speed along the steel tracks straight to the paradise of Communism.

133

Driving this locomotive of state would be the handsome model engineer, glamorized slightly, to represent the whole of the clear-eyed, purposeful, Communist-Party-loving Han people. Li Chi was sure that the picture would be his cultural and political masterpiece of socialist art. Humbly, he offered to paint this picture during whatever time he could be spared from his commune labors. He asked only for some sharply clear photographs of the model engineer and the locomotive.

Li Chi was fairly sure that no really adequate photographs were available. Furthermore, his letter was of the type that officials could not accept in any halfway manner; they would either have to disregard it altogether or make a large production of it —at least to the extent of sending him to the city where the engineer—and Miss Fei—lived so that the locomotive and the young man could be painted properly from life. The letter was addressed to the commune's propaganda director. Li Chi knew that this official would have no authority concerning the "Love Your Locomotive" campaign, and he therefore would pass the letter on to his superior. If the superior had the courage to make a negative decision, Li Chi's slender hope of a visit with Miss Fei was doomed. More likely, however, was the possibility that the superior would send on the letter to *his* superior for a decision. In this manner, the letter might well go up the chain of command until it just happened to fall on the desk of an official who had some responsibility for the "Love Your Locomotive" campaign and who just happened to be rather desperately short of new publicity angles.

In any case, this is just what did happen. The process took nearly three weeks, and Li Chi had given up in despair. Late one afternoon, however, he was called in from the fields to the office of the commune's propaganda officer. There he learned that he was ordered by a Peking official with an impressive title to paint the suggested masterpiece of socialist art. To ensure proper socialist realism, the picture was to be painted from life, and Li Chi therefore was to proceed forthwith to the city where the engineer lived. The necessary authority for the travel expenses and the travel permit were attached.

Understandably, Li Chi was elated, and his feeling of self-satisfaction was justified. As he left the office, however, the propaganda officer said to Li Chi, almost as an afterthought, "This sort of assignment, of course, is authorized only on the understanding that you can be spared from your present duties. Hence, as a matter of routine, you ought to obtain from Comrade Ho an official temporary release."

Li Chi's spirits sagged. He was right back where he had started. He knew that Comrade Ho would never sign the release. Preventing Li Chi from having a pleasant holiday in the South would become a matter of "face" for the Party Secretary. He would claim that Li Chi's services were needed desperately for the planting season, and he would picture Li Chi as an unregenerate, unreliable, undeserving type who needed close supervision. Ultimately the matter would become a contest between Comrade Ho's authority and that of the high official. Comrade Ho naturally would lose, but by that time the "Love Your Locomotive" campaign would be over.

Two hours later, Li Chi entered the shed where the political discussion meetings of his *hsia fang* group were held. He was depressed, but the germ of an idea was forming in his head. As soon as Comrade Ho brought the meeting to order, Li Chi asked for permission to speak. "Before the discussion begins," he said, "I should like to request the advice and guidance of the Party and my fellow discussion-group members on a personal problem."

A hush fell on the group. No one had ever before heard Li Chi speak at a meeting without first being prodded; even worse, no one could even imagine Li Chi asking for advice from anyone. Comrade Ho's little mouth made a perfect "O" in astonishment. "Well, now, this is a surprise," he said finally. "The problem must be serious indeed if our famous artist needs help."

Li Chi shrugged. "I have been ordered by a deputy director

of the Propaganda Department in Peking to leave this commune for about ten days in order to paint a certain picture," Li Chi said. "I should like advice on how to refuse to obey this order from such a high official in our government." He passed the Peking letter to Comrade Ho.

As the Party secretary read the letter, a look of suspicion came over his face. He studied Li Chi for a moment. "A pleasant journey to the warm South. An easy, leisurely assignment. The pleasures and comforts of a city," Comrade Ho said. "Do you expect us to believe you want to refuse this order?"

Again Li Chi shrugged. "That's what I'm asking your help for," he said. "I'm a peasant, don't forget. I prefer the countryside."

"That hardly is an argument we can give to a deputy director in Peking, is it?" Ho said.

"No," Li Chi said, "but as a peasant I understand the importance of the planting season. No seed in the ground, no food in the pot. I do not doubt that the 'Love Your Locomotive' campaign also is important, but surely an artist with a proletarian background would be better for this assignment."

"Would you question the judgment of the deputy director?" Comrade Ho asked. "If he had thought that another person was preferable, he would have given that person the assignment."

"But why is it necessary to leave here?" Li Chi said. "I think I could paint the picture just as well from photographs. Staying here would save the government the expense of my journey and allow a more important cadre to use my seat."

Comrade Ho shook his head. "That argument, in effect, accuses the deputy director of stupidity. He knows about the travel situation, and we can be sure he knows that pictures can be painted from photos."

Li Chi allowed a slight note of desperation to creep into his voice. "I would miss some very important group meetings here," he said. "Just when I was finally beginning to understand why it was that we could be so hungry and cold last winter when, in reality, our country was enjoying unparalleled prosperity. And now when we are being given revelation on our beloved Mao's brilliant ideas concerning antirevisionism—"

Comrade Ho leaned back in his chair, and again his mouth made an "O" of astonishment. The others gasped aloud in surprise. Here was Li Chi making correct statements, admitting to Party influence, and in fact sounding exactly like everyone else. No one really believed he meant what he said, and a few were secretly sorry to see the last of the great individualists wither away like this. The majority, however, rejoiced to hear their normally recalcitrant colleague now reciting the lesson so properly, and they felt that a sinner had been brought to repentance.

Nevertheless, Comrade Ho was not entirely fooled. When he recovered from his surprise, he began to suspect that Li Chi was trying to trick him. Craftily the idea did occur to him that Li Chi might really want to go on the assignment and was using elaborate deception tactics to get Ho's release. He quickly marshaled in his mind the arguments and phrases whereby a proper and acceptable refusal of the assignment could be made by Li Chi. He felt that he could test Li Chi's real intentions by pointing out these proper arguments. He pointed a finger at the artist. "Your excuses are weak. They won't do," he began, and paused to choose his next words carefully.

Before he could continue, Miss Sung jumped up and interrupted him. In her enthusiasn, as it sometimes happened, she got the wrong cue. "I think Mr. Li Chi *should examine his conscience* for the *real* reason he does not want to accept this assignment," she said. She gave him a look of smug righteousness and sat down primly.

Li Chi pretended that her words had struck deep and that he could no longer hide his secrets from these people who understood him so thoroughly. "I confess I do have other reasons," he said in a gloomy voice. "As you know, being a peasant myself, I overcame the barrier of the masses much easier than any of you. In fact I have become friendly enough with the peasants so that they often give me bits of extra food. Thus I manage to live here in what amounts to the lap of luxury. I could expect no such advantages in a strange and distant city." He hung his head in shame. "But that's not all. I happen to suffer from sea-sickness, and the prospect of the long boat trip down the river to the railway line fills me with dread—"

"Ah *hah!*" exclaimed Deputy Secretary Lo.

"The truth is out!" Miss Sung said, the note of virtuous triumph unmistakable in her voice.

Comrade Ho pursed his lips into a little rosebud. He was worried. Perhaps Li Chi really did not want to take the assignment. In that case, the somewhat dangerous effort whereby Ho would pit his puny authority against that of a deputy director in Peking would be wasted. He considered for only a moment, and then wrote rapidly on a slip of paper. Finally, he handed the paper and the Peking letter back to Li Chi. "My conscience forbids me from allowing you to disobey your orders," he said. "Here is the temporary release from your present duties. You will take tomorrow's boat."

"I make myself a willing tool of the Party," Li Chi said, accepting the papers. He did not attempt to hide his triumph, and he saw the startled look on Ho's face as the Party Secretary realized he had been tricked.

The weather in the southern city was most pleasant. Li Chi arrived in the early evening, but he went immediately in search of Miss Fei. He found her at the shop where she painted the pottery. She had worked late, she told him, in order to get well ahead on her assignments and thus have more free time to spend with him. To Li Chi she looked just as beautiful as she had at the Art Institute, and all the pain and pleasure of his first love returned to him. He escorted her home, but he lost his way in the strange city, and finally stopped to rest with her on a deserted section of a pleasant canal. It was after midnight when she slipped quietly into her dormitory, and he returned to his

138

hotel. Contented and soothed, he looked forward to another nine days of bliss.

The next morning, however, he was distressed to learn that the local Party Committee, overcome with their success in making a national hero of their model engineer, had sent him on a tour of the country. No one could say precisely where he was at the moment or where he would be at any specified time. Under these circumstances, it was not possible to paint a picture from life, and the officials could suggest only that Li Chi return at once to the commune.

The prospect of being denied the other nine days with Miss Fei was too difficult for Li Chi to accept. He felt that he was *morally* entitled to them by virtue of the effort and ingenuity he had expended to win them. This feeling helped to increase his persuasiveness. First he convinced the officials that the Peking authorities would be dangerously angered if they learned that Li Chi, world-famous artist, had been sent here on a wild-goose chase. And, second, he convinced them that they would win twice as much prestige if they could have *two* engineer heroes from their city.

The officials were willing enough to cooperate, but the only other locomotive engineer who lived in the city was a wrinkled, scrawny old man whose front teeth were missing. He had been retired from active duty years previously, but out of respect for his age and his experience he still held a nominal position of some importance in the association for railway workers. He was hardly the stuff, however, from which heroes could be made, and Li Chi faced defeat.

Nevertheless, the old engineer was made of sterner stuff than Li Chi realized and upon hearing Li Chi's problem suggested a possible solution. The campaign, he pointed out, was to teach love for the *locomotive,* not for the engineer. It was the engine that tirelessly, uncomplainingly, did all the work, while the engineer merely pushed buttons and pulled a few levers. Thus a particular locomotive—a particularly *worthy* locomotive—

should be chosen to have its story told and its portrait painted. It just so happened that the old man knew where such a locomotive could be found, and he arranged to introduce Li Chi to it the next day.

Li Chi took Miss Fei with him when he met the old man the next day. The engineer said nothing when he was introduced to the girl; he stared at her for a long, awkward moment and then, to Li Chi's surprise, tears began to roll down the old man's wrinkled cheeks.

"Miss Fei," he said in a shaky voice, "Miss Fei, don't you remember me? It was the happiest day of my life."

Understanding lighted the girl's face. "You worked for my grandfather," she said.

The old man nodded, the tears still streaming down his face. "He was one of the top men in the railways during the old regime, but when I retired he came in person to congratulate me. He brought you with him—"

Miss Fei squeezed the old man's hand.

"And now," he said, smiling and wiping away his tears, "your great family honors me again. Fate has sent you to give me the help I need so badly."

Li Chi was doubtful that anyone could help the old man when he saw the locomotive. It stood among high weeds on a siding and was the sorriest excuse for a locomotive Li Chi had ever seen. It seemed to sag in every direction; it was covered with rust and obviously had not moved for years. Nevertheless, the engineer was hugely proud of it; he himself, he said, used to be its driver and he knew its every nut and bolt and every square inch of its iron carcass. He swore that with the help of someone young and vigorous he could bring the engine back to such life as to make it the envy of the entire transportation system. Obviously, the old man had not been able to talk any of the younger railway workers into helping him; Li Chi and Miss Fei, however, had no choice but to follow their new friend's enthusiasm. The old man easily obtained permission from the local railway authorities to do what he could about making the engine operative again.

The next week was devoted to feverish activity. Li Chi fixed up a room for himself in a barn near where the locomotive stood. By using sometimes the authority of the Peking letter, sometimes his power of persuasion, by a little judicious cannibalizing, some outright pilfering, and a great deal of improvisation, the necessary parts for the engine were obtained. The engineer worked almost without eating or sleeping, using Li Chi's sharper eyes and steadier hands as his own. Miss Fei spent all her waking hours (and perhaps some of the others as well) with Li Chi and the old man. She prepared food, straightened up the room, and saw to it generally that Li Chi was well taken care of. She also took pictures and made sketches so that a "before and after" record of their effort would be available. When she had nothing else to do she chipped rust and polished brass.

In spite of himself, Li Chi found excitement in the rebirth of this old monster of the rails. He was both thrilled and impressed with the fearsome way it belched steam and smoke. He conceived the idea of painting his feelings about the locomotive on the locomotive itself. He thought of it as a ferocious steam-belching tiger who devoured space and time between the present and a happier future. Thus, with the use of a little sheet metal, much paint, many suggestions from Miss Fei, and a lot of skill, he and the old man transformed the whole front of the engine into a huge leaping tiger. On the rest of the body were pictured the mountains and plains through which the train would pass and the fruit and grain the train would haul. Unquestionably, the locomotive was the most startling and colorful piece of railway equipment ever to ride the Chinese rails. The job took two weeks, but no one objected.

At first, the old man had been doubtful about the artwork on the engine—it had seemed to him like gilding a lily—but he accepted it readily enough when he understood the value of it for campaign publicity. In fact, it was he who made the biggest sacrifice that added the crowning touch to the project. Li Chi knew that the old man had been anticipating the moment when he could handle the controls that would move his beloved monster out again onto the main line, "But who wants to see an ugly old turtle like me?" he had asked. Thereupon he had begun at once to teach Miss Fei the process of driving the huge engine.

Only a small crowd of obviously bored newsmen and railway officials showed up for the ceremony at the station on the day that the refurbished locomotive returned to duty. They stiffened with astonishment, however, when that extraordinary engine puffed powerfully into view. The drama of the moment was much increased by the sight of that huge and frighteningly brawny brute under the confident control of a beautiful girl. Li Chi saw with amusement that Miss Fei, underneath her seeming nonchalance, was enjoying every minute of her task. Suddenly a spontaneous cheer burst from the group on the platform. Li Chi knew that the iron tiger was going to become a showpiece of the "Love Your Locomotive" campaign.*

Li Chi saw that the old man was shaking with emotion and that tears were streaming down his face again. "It was a magnificent sacrifice of yours to let Miss Fei drive your locomotive," he said, patting the man's shoulders.

"It was the least I could do for her," the engineer replied. He

* The amount of truth in this episode is impossible to estimate. At first, in the campaign, engineers were publicized. Later, however, a specific engine became the "hero." It was called "The Mao Tse-tung." If the propaganda is to be believed, the engine ran almost entirely on the love it received from its engineers. It rarely needed fuel or the replacement of worn-out parts. Moreover, it evidently was capable not only of pulling incredibly heavy loads for many thousands of miles each day; it could also be in several parts of the country at the same time. Occasionally "The Mao Tse-tung" was described as being painted and adorned; perhaps, therefore, Li Chi's engine became absorbed in the "master hero." Few of the regime's campaigns, however, were ever accepted by the masses with such magnificent indifference.

brushed the tears from his cheeks. "And I don't mean that because her grandfather was once kind to me. I did it because she and I are the only people in this stupid campaign who really do love our locomotive!"

CHAPTER XII

The Pig

Li Chi could endure almost any kind of privation. He never noticed the furnishings of his quarters. He seemed oblivious to extremes of weather, winter or summer. And he was indifferent to the quality and even the quantity of the food he was given. He did have, however, one weakness: tobacco. He felt that life was hardly worth living without at least ten cigarettes a day to smoke.

Inevitably, Comrade Party Secretary Ho became aware of Li Chi's weakness. It was equally inevitable that the Party Secretary would attempt to exploit the weakness. One should understand, however, that the fat comrade was not consciously vindictive; very seldom was he guilty of a malicious act without first having worked out the most elaborate rationalizations. Thus Comrade Ho took great pains to convince himself that Li Chi, despite an enviable proletarian background, had somehow allowed his political thinking to lag behind. In other words, Li Chi's political level, alas, had sunk below that reached by the masses, and he therefore stood in grave danger of an infection of rightist thoughts. Thus, for his own salvation, Li Chi needed help in having his political level raised.

As Comrade Mao had proven (scientifically no doubt), confession and atonement through an act of contrition in which the flesh was mortified were the most effective means of stimulating an increase in political consciousness. Hence, Li Chi was sure to derive great benefit if the masses, say, were to deprive him of the right to purchase cigarettes for a week or two. Comrade Ho did not doubt that he could make the masses see their duty in this respect. Moreover, the obvious time in which to bring up the matter would be at the first of the coming "Summary of the Harvest Season" discussion-group meetings. Ho's mouth stretched into a tight little smile of happy anticipation.

The purpose of these particular meetings was not really to summarize the achievements of the harvest season, but rather to spread the Party's camouflage around the fact that this year's harvest had been even worse than last year's and that consumer goods were becoming noticeably even more scarce. Comrade Ho opened the first meeting with a neat little speech based on Chairman Mao's words "from the masses and to the masses." The Party Secretary appealed to the masses (in this case, the discussion-group members) to give the Party (in this case, him) the benefit of their wisdom in the form of their comments on the current concrete situation. "If you expect the Party to give you guidance during these meetings, you will be disappointed," he said in conclusion. "It is the Party that now expects guidance from you."

There was a long silence while each of the "masses" modestly waited for someone else to begin guiding the Party. Finally, Miss Sung put up her hand and the others breathed easier, for the silence had begun to be awkward. "The current concrete situation appears infinitely promising . . ." she began, but then shyness overcame her and she could say no more. Nevertheless, Comrade Ho considered the comment as though hearing it now for the first time in his life. He seemed almost to "taste" it experimentally for the delicacy of its subtle wisdom. Finally, he actually beamed with delight and admiration at the sheer brilliance of this contribution from the masses.

The masses still, however, tended to remain mute. Ultimately, Deputy Secretary Lo helped matters along by quoting from a magazine he happened to have with him. "The present harvest is expected to yield 28.13 percent more food than last year's record-breaking crop," he read. A gasp was heard from the group and then a splatter of applause. Smiling even more happily, Comrade Ho nodded in confirmation of this happy statistic. He placed a pudgy finger alongside his button nose and winked slowly; this implied that he had known the truth all along but had wanted to save it as a pleasant surprise. Now that the cat was out of the bag, however, he himself read a quotation from an official publication that looked like the *People's Daily*. "The purchasing power of the peasants has been raised by the unheard-of figure of"—here he paused to look up with an expression of utter astonishment—*"two point six eight percent!"* The gasp from the group was even louder than before, and now the applause was thunderous. Miss Sung, overcome with emotion, jumped up to say in a trembling voice that the Chinese peasant had achieved the highest living standard the world had ever seen.

The pattern of the thinking of the masses in summary of the harvest season was now becoming clear. Practically every member of the group could have written the rest of the report, and each report would have been identical. Inevitably, however, at least one member allowed emotion momentarily to cloud his judgment to the extent that his comment struck a discordant note. For example, Mr. Wong from the music department, the father of four, gave a heartrending account of the suffering of the children during the period of shortages the previous year— and the year before that. He was implying what everyone knew—namely, that the shortages this year also would be bad—and he pleaded that the authorities give thought to the health of the next generation by ensuring adequate nourishment for the children during the months ahead.

By the time he finished, the group was silent again. The members scarcely breathed. Comrade Ho's smile had faded as he listened and his face had become sad; now he turned to the others and spread his hands, voicelessly pleading with them for help.

Miss Sung stood up and stated that what they had just heard was a man who had deliberately "detached himself from the Party," who actually "distrusted the Party" and had put himself into "opposition" to it. She demanded that Mr. Wong *examine his conscience* for rightism. Taking her cue, others began accusing poor Mr. Wong of even more serious crimes. He had grown pale, and beads of perspiration were visible on his forehead.

Finally Comrade Ho humbly interposed himself into the discussion. After stating that the Party was always subjected wholly to the will of the masses, he added modestly that the Party in its posture of eternal vigilance had acquired a certain expertise on rightism and rightists and could speak on these subjects with some authority. At this, Comrade Ho snapped his fingers at his deputy, who immediately placed an open file on the Party Secretary's desk. Comrade Ho thereupon read from the minutes of a meeting of the same discussion group ten months previously. The *unanimous* decision of the members had been that all the talk about the so-called shortages had been nothing but rightist slander and imperialist lies. Mr. Wong, in using the word "shortages," indicated that he was duped innocently by the imperialists and their rightist agents. Comrade Ho besought Mr. Wong to repudiate the vicious propaganda of the foreign devils, and to re-energize his vigilance against rightism. Mr. Wong, visibly relieved, nodded enthusiastically.

Turning to the others, Comrade Ho reminded them that the purpose of the meeting was for the masses to give guidance to the Party. In this connection, he said, Mr. Wong had made an invaluable contribution. Mr. Wong had suggested that the Party

147

should give thought and consideration to the health of the next generation by seeing that the children of today were adequately looked after. The Party deeply appreciated this suggestion, and as a reward Mr. Wong would be placed on the commune's Honor Roll. Henceforth, Mr. Wong would have the opportunity to hasten his political progress by two extra hours of work a day, the work to be of a latrine-cleaning nature. Spontaneously, the other group members crowded around Mr. Wong to congratulate him and thereby show their admiration and envy. Mr. Wong stated that he would be eternally grateful to the Party for its compassion, patience, understanding, and generosity.

Thereafter, no more rightist thoughts were expressed, and if no one else achieved the Honor Roll, the "guidance" from the "masses" was at least clear and familiar. Furthermore, only Li Chi needed to express his approval of the customary formulas, and the report of the group would be unanimous. For the meeting's last hour, Li Chi had been slumped down in his chair, asleep with a dead cigarette dangling from his lips. Comrade Ho now stated that perhaps they should all tiptoe out quietly so that Li Chi's rest would not be disturbed. To indicate that this was a joke, the Party Secretary winked broadly, and the others tittered nervously. At the mention of his name, Li Chi awakened. He yawned and stretched. "What do you want from me?" he asked.

"We would be honored if we could have your comments on, criticism of, or queries about this group's report concerning an estimate of the harvest situation," Comrade Ho said.

"Harvest!" Li Chi exclaimed. "Why bother to discuss it? We all know that the production this year will be average."

"No, I didn't know. Nor, I might add, does the commune Party Secretary," Ho said, "nor even the Provincial Party Secretary; in fact, not even Chairman Mao Tse-tung knows what the production of this year's harvest will be. But you, Mr. Li Chi, have this vital information. Perhaps you will share it with us?

Perhaps you will tell us what you mean by an 'average' harvest?"

Li Chi shrugged. "The harvest this year will be worse than last year's," he said, "but it will be better than next year's. Average. Any peasant knows that. All you have to do is ask."

Comrade Ho closed his eyes, drew a great shuddering breath, and then, suddenly, smacked the table with the palm of his hand. Next, he opened his eyes wide, because he perceived that for the first time his adversary had slipped. "In other words, Mr. Li Chi," Ho said, and his voice was as smooth as heavy oil, "you apparently prophesy food *shortages*. . . ."

"I prophesy nothing," Li Chi replied. "Even if we produce a superabundance, I can't have any of it because I haven't any money. I never learned to manage my financial affairs sensibly. It was because my family was too poor to teach me such things—"

"I notice that regardless of how little money you have, you always manage to afford cigarettes." Comrade Ho's voice was a purr, but his face maintained an expression of innocence. "Perhaps, therefore, you are expert enough to comment on the tobacco industry for our report."

Li Chi seemed only now to notice that the dead cigarette was still in the corner of his mouth. He took it out, looked at it in disgust, and threw it on the floor. "Cigarettes are getting harder to obtain. Why? And don't tell me it is because of the increased purchasing power of the masses. We can purchase less than we ever could, but still the quality has been growing steadily worse for the last two years, and this means the quantity of available tobacco has been decreasing. I suggest that you Communists find out who is responsible for this mess, punish the guilty one, and make the necessary arrangements for correcting the situation."

There was an unnatural gleam in Ho's eyes, but his face took on a look of indignation. "What you have said is almost a classic example of 'failure to trust the Communist Party,' " he said. He pointed a pudgy finger at Li Chi. "You have no way of knowing anything about the tobacco industry, its problems, difficulties, the tireless efforts, and the achievements of the comrades in charge, yet you have only destructive criticism and negative suggestions to offer. Your attitude is typically reactionary."

The word "reactionary" was the cue; now the other group members hastened to voice their criticism of the person who had been designated by the authority as reprehensible. Li Chi yawned again and slumped down into his chair. He seemed resigned to wait patiently for the storm of abuse to subside. Slowly, however, Li Chi sat up as he perceived the direction in which Ho was pushing the discussion. Finally, it was Miss Sung who found the right track. She suggested that Li Chi might learn increased respect for the noble Party members, cadres, and workers of the tobacco industry if he were denied the right to purchase cigarettes from the commune's stores for a period of two weeks. Comrade Ho announced that the masses, in their wisdom, had reached a decision and had passed sentence. Li Chi now was genuinely worried—the idea of going even one day without a cigarette filled him with anguish. The look of triumph on Comrade Ho's face was unmistakable.

The Party Secretary's triumph, however, was short-lived. Word of Li Chi's predicament went quickly through the village. Everyone knew about his addiction to tobacco, and sympathy for him was widespread. Once again, Li Chi was surprised and touched by the number of genuine friends he had. The other members of his production team, together, managed to part with six cigarettes a day for him. The old farmer in whose house he lived contrived to get two more a day from an undisclosed source. Lo Fu, the peasant whose painting Li Chi had supported in Peking, was able to deliver a whole handful at irregular intervals.

Thus the fact that Li Chi would somehow manage to obtain

enough cigarettes became obvious on the third day after he **was** denied the right to purchase them from the commune's stores. Strictly speaking, Comrade Ho did not lose face because, according to the record, the decision to punish Li Chi had been made by his fellow group members and not by the Party Secretary. Nevertheless, Comrade Ho knew that practically everyone in the village was secretly laughing at him, and he was infuriated.

At the same time, however, he understood that certain aspects of the situation were extremely dangerous for him, and for this reason he was forced to be cautious. The tobacco shortage being what it was, the generosity of Li Chi's friends represented genuine sacrifice, and it provided startlingly unexpected proof of Li Chi's popularity with the masses. The Communist leaders had always shown an almost pathological fear of even the most insignificant kind of *united* opposition to their authority, and they would go to any extreme to prevent it from arising. Unofficially, they regarded as their most dangerous enemy any individual who was not completely subservient to and identified with the Party's authority but who nevertheless had the support of some group within the masses.

Li Chi certainly was not identified with the Party in any way; to a small extent he had been martyred by the Party, and out of sympathy for him, a group within the masses was, in effect, uniting against the will of the Party. The unity might be only temporary and the action trivial, but from such tiny political sparks huge social conflagrations were quite possible. The Communist authorities knew this well, and if apprised of the situation concerning Li Chi, they would take prompt and decisive action. Part of this action would be directed against Comrade Ho, who had been responsible for the circumstances from which the deplorable situation arose. Thus, Comrade Ho would make every effort to prevent his superiors from learning about the situation. Moreover, despite his anger and his desire to see Li Chi suffer, he knew that he should immediately end Li Chi's martyrdom by allowing him official access to the commune's limited supply of cigarettes.

The defeat, however, was hard for the Party Secretary to accept, and this made him susceptible to an alternative that suggested itself to him suddenly in a flash of true inspiration. Comrade Ho had a niece who was the principal of an elementary school in a city about a hundred miles distant. Recently she had written to him to ask if any of his *hsia fang* professors might be spared to give guest lectures to her pupils. Comrade Ho did not doubt that the pupils would benefit greatly from about ten days of lectures on art from Li Chi. Ho knew that the artist had no money, and pay day was ten days away. Vouchers for travel, lodging, and basic food could be provided, but tobacco would have to be purchased separately. In a city where Li Chi was a stranger, the likelihood that people would give him cigarettes or lend him money to buy them was nil.

Li Chi was called from the fields early next morning, given the lecture assignment, and told to catch the morning train. He had barely time to pack his few possessions. He guessed the real purpose behind the assignment, and was greatly perturbed. He had exactly three cigarettes left—barely enough for the five-hour train trip—and he could visualize no means of obtaining more. As he rushed out the door of his quarters, he almost stumbled over his pig. On impulse, he picked it up and carried it with him under his arm.

The pig was a leftover from a short period during the previous year when official policy encouraged private pig-raising. The piglet Li Chi had drawn was deficient in some basic way; it ate well enough, but it grew very slowly and never seemed to put on flesh or fat. It was so stunted and skinny that when the time had come to sell the pig, the government buyer had refused it as being not worth the cost of transportation to the packing plant. Since then, Li Chi had kept the pig simply because he did not know what else to do with it. He had long since acquired the habit of foraging food for the animal, but the pig remained a miserable specimen of its breed. It was still under Li Chi's arm when he reported to Comrade Ho's niece at the city school.

Whereas Comrade Ho was repulsively fat, his niece was pleasingly plump; moreover, she had the large, luminous eyes and shapely eyebrows that Li Chi always found particularly attractive. She was in her office surrounded by a group of students when he entered. He stared at her with such uninhibited admiration that she was rendered speechless with embarrassment, and the children soon began to giggle. At the sound, Li Chi turned to them smiling. "You are wondering why I travel with this fine pig," he said. "It is because I am trying to help out with our country's agricultural problem. Did you know that our government has officially proclaimed that a pig is actually a small fertilizer factory? The more pigs we have, the more fertilizer will be absorbed by the ground and the more crops will grow, thereby providing for more pigs whose fertilizer will produce even more crops. Somewhere in there, you will agree, is the formula for untold riches."

Now the children laughed out loud. "We know," one of them said. "We have studied this. . . ."

"It is not a laughing matter," the pretty principal said. Li Chi was aware, however, that she was trying to suppress a smile. "But this must be the famous artist who has come to tell us how to make pretty pictures. Judging from his pig, I should guess that he can teach us more about drawing pigs than raising them."

In smiling protest, Li Chi put down the pig so that it could be seen better. "Admittedly the pig is not handsome," Li Chi said; although he addressed the children, he was really talking to the principal. "But he *is* lovable."

At that moment, however, the poor pig, apparently confused by all this unaccustomed attention and praise, now attempted to fertilize the office floor. The children began to laugh uproariously. "Also, you must admit that this pig is absolutely undaunted by any obstacle," Li Chi said, and in spite of herself the principal laughed.

The laughter stopped abruptly, however, with the entrance of a young but wizened little man whom Li Chi immediately recognized as a typical Party cadre. Devoid of a sense of humor or any imagination, the cadre would consider laughter merely an expression of indiscipline. Without imagination, however, he could accept a situation only as it was presented to him. Thus, Li Chi picked up the pig, acting as though carrying pigs in school was a perfectly normal everyday function, and the cadre lacked the wit to make an issue of it. Li Chi learned that the man was not only the school's vice-principal but also its Party Secretary, and thus the real authority in the institution. Li Chi was told to attend a staff meeting that would be held immediately after classes.

Li Chi was still carrying the pig when he entered the Party Secretary's office for the meeting a half hour later. Here, the pig was an unnatural element that could detract from the dignity and therefore the authority of the Party Secretary, who thus was forced to recognize the pig as a problem. "Animals," he stated to Li Chi, "belong outside. People, inside."

"If arrangements can be made to have my pig looked after and fed, I shall gladly take him outside," Li Chi answered.

The Party Secretary made a visible effort to control exasperation. "Pigs are an aspect of agriculture that is the responsibility of the communes. Education is the responsibility of the schools," he said.

"You are wondering why I brought this pig with me from the commune," Li Chi said. "It is because I was one of those who, last year, volunteered to serve our country's needs by engaging in private pig-raising."

"Such so-called sideline operations were an aspect of decadent capitalism, in that limited private profiteering was permitted," the Party Secretary said. "The operations were introduced as a temporary expedient only and have long since been abandoned."

"Precisely," Li Chi answered. "It has been the official change in policy that has forced me, as a matter of ideological principle, to retain my pig." Li Chi saw that the Party Secretary, as well as the others, was confused, and he therefore explained: "You will recall that when we were asked to undertake a sideline operation to aid the advance toward socialism, we private pig raisers had to forage for feed. When we could find none we had to buy it, and the price was often very high. Nevertheless, some were able to sell their fattened pigs at a profit. Others took a loss, but either way they were operating under capitalistic laws of which profit and loss are basic aspects."

The Party Secretary now lost his patience. "Mr. Li Chi," he said, "we are not holding this meeting to listen to your discourse on elementary political economy—"

But Li Chi ignored the interruption, and continued: "Naturally our government did not permit these capitalistic ways to continue. Soon the government was selling the feed for the pigs at a fixed price, and the raisers were made to sell their fattened animals to a government buyer—also at a fixed price. I'm sure the two prices were worked out fairly so that neither profit nor loss was involved. This pig, however, lived through the government's capitalist policy when I had to pay a high price for feed. If I sold him now to the government for the fixed price, I would take a loss."

The room had become silent. "Just what do you expect to do with this pig?" the Party Secretary asked finally.

"Naturally, I expect to keep him until our government sees fit to pay me enough so that my investment is realized—not a cent more, not a cent less."

The Party Secretary banged the desk with his fist. "Nonsense!" he said. "We raised pigs here at the school during that campaign, and when we sold them to the government buyer we took a small loss on some of them. What difference does it make?" He pointed at Li Chi. "Tomorrow morning, you will take that pig to the government buyer before classes and sell it for whatever the buyer gives you. If the price represents a loss, you can consider it a small contribution from you to socialist construction."

Li Chi gave every indication of being deeply shocked. "Comrade Party Secretary!" he exclaimed, "do you mean to sit there and admit that you actually took a loss in selling your pigs? Don't you know that that is decidedly against Party policy? Is *this* the attitude toward Party policy you encourage around here?"

The man wavered. "What do you mean?" he asked.

Li Chi knew now that he had won. "It is not enough to know simply that our country is against capitalism; one must understand *why* we reject it," he said. "Capitalism is based on the economic principle of profit and loss; the capitalists exploit the masses by extracting the profit that is the masses' loss. When you—or I—make a profit we are exploiting our people and their vanguard the Party. But when we permit our government to inflict loss upon us, we are saying, in effect, that the Communist Party of our country is no better than the capitalist gangsters—that it *exploits* the masses. Imagine what our great leaders would think and feel to find that *proof* of such exploitation actually exists. Imagine the disillusionment such news would cause in the capitals of the neutral countries. Imagine the cynical propaganda the imperialists could make of it. . . . Really, comrade, I am distressed"—Li Chi shook his head sadly—"deeply distressed." He got up slowly and, still carrying the pig, left the office.

Li Chi knew, of course, that he never would have been able to get away with these arguments if he had been alone with the Party Secretary. Only in front of subordinates would the pretense of strict adherence to ideology be necessary. Li Chi did not have long to wait. The Party Secretary appeared and handed him a paper. "Write down the amount you would need to receive for that pig so that you will have neither profit nor loss," the Party Secretary said. "I will see that you get it. . . ."

The figure Li Chi jotted down would pay for all the cigarettes he wanted until his next pay day, and it included a little extra for something—he had not yet decided what—that might entice a plumply pretty school principal.

CHAPTER XIII

The Innovations Sweepstakes

When Li Chi returned to the commune, he found that his quarters had been moved from the peasant hut of the production team leader to a crowded dormitory that he was to share with seven other instructors from the Normal College. Because fuel was unobtainable, the room promised to be miserably cold, as well as crowded, that winter. When Li Chi found further that he would no longer be permitted to work with the production team, but instead was assigned to odd jobs with the other college instructors, he felt that he would be putting up with all the disadvantages of *hsia fang* without having any of its advantages. He decided, therefore, to get himself assigned back to the city, where he would have more opportunity for painting.

When he attended the first meeting of his discussion group, he found that the topic was "Overcoming the Barrier of the

Masses." Li Chi surmised that this topic was connected in some way with the fact that he was now being denied "contact with the masses"; he therefore listened carefully as Comrade Ho manipulated the discussion according to the instruction he had received from his Party superiors. From the comments, Li Chi gathered that the authorities were dissatisfied with the propaganda job the *hsia fang* people had been doing on the peasants. Apparently the fact that the peasants were uncooperative, sullen, and openly contemptuous of the cadres was just becoming known to the Communist leaders. According to the dogma, however, the peasants should love the Party fervently. As is customary with the Communists when reality opposes dogma, reality is subverted. To the Communists, however, there is nothing illogical in denying an unpleasant truth, and at the same time seeking to put the blame for the unpleasant truth upon someone else. Thus, at the very time when much publicity in the papers was "proving" how deeply the peasants loved and respected the Party, the discussion groups were being informed that the peasants' disaffection was due to the peasants' ignorance and political backwardness—and to the fact that the *hsia fang* people had failed to "educate" them adequately.

When Li Chi was asked to comment on the situation, he spared no one's feelings. "Naturally, you have not overcome the 'barrier of the masses,' and it's not surprising that the peasants despise you," he said. "You never really made any attempt to know them or to help them. You only talked about it. You only pretended to work. You may fool the authorities about how much you did here, but you did not fool the peasants."

Comrade Ho's face had grown purple; his fists were clenched and his breath came in explosive little puffs from his rosebud mouth. When he could speak, he pointed a thick finger at Li Chi. "But you—you of course overcame the barrier of the masses completely. I suppose you gave an ideological education to every peasant you came in contact with."

Li Chi shrugged. "I didn't even think about it," he said. "I identified myself completely with the masses, and we worked hard together to serve construction."

Comrade Ho leaned forward. "You admit you gave nothing of ideological value to the masses, but perhaps you learned something of ideological importance from *them?*"

"I learned to love the people I worked with as though they were my own family," Li Chi replied. "If that is of ideological importance, then I learned much."

Comrade Ho leaned back, and although his smile was sad his air of triumph was unmistakable. " 'Family love and family self-fishness undermine socialist construction,' " he quoted; " 'individualism is the enemy of revolution.' "

With this cue, the others now jumped in to attack Li Chi; they were not in the least hesitant because Li Chi's record at the commune had been so annoyingly perfect that the chance to blot it was pleasant. Thus his "bourgeois sentimentality" was condemned in the strongest terms. "We are given this glorious *hsia fang* opportunity in order to achieve ideological remolding through learning from the masses," Comrade Ho said, to show that he approved of the criticism. "We are not sent here to be corrupted by the peasants' political backwardness."

"I should like to ask Mr. Li Chi to *examine his conscience,*" Miss Sung said, "to see if he is not 'unprincipled in his dealing with the masses.' " Comrade Ho beamed at her, and she cast Li Chi a look in which smugness and reproach were equally apparent.

"Do I understand then that all of you feel that Mr. Li Chi's *hsia fang* should be extended indefinitely until he has learned the elements of socialist enlightenment?" Comrade Ho asked.

When the others had chorused their confirmation, Li Chi stood up. "I am in wholehearted agreement with the decision of this group," he said. "At least my record here shows that I can make a genuine contribution to construction by working with the peasants. After all, I at least have crossed the barrier of the masses. I shall be with the people I love—"

Comrade Ho struck the desk with his fist. "Stop!" he shouted. At this point, after two years, he now suddenly came to the conclusion that Li Chi really did prefer to work at the commune; he accepted finally that Li Chi had been tricking the authorities all this time. "You are not going to get away with this any longer," Comrade Ho said. "You're an unregenerate backward element. The *hsia fang* opportunity is wasted on you. You will go back to the college tomorrow—"

Unfortunately Li Chi was unable to enjoy his little triumph for more than a few hours. Apparently the authorities had already decided that the *hsia fang* opportunity was wasted on all of Comrade Ho's group. Or perhaps it was simply that the group, which had been made to spend about twice as much time in the countryside as the average *hsia fang* people, was considered to have completed their turn. In any case, the group was told the next day to return to the Normal College in Wuhu, and Li Chi made the trip back with the others.

At the Normal College they found that conditions had changed drastically. The authorities had finally faced the fact that the attempt to accelerate the educational program had done more harm than good. Hence the emphasis had shifted back from "red" to "expert." This meant that the best teachers were now given some authority and respect, even if they came from the bourgeoisie or were guilty of being "ideologically backward."

These were circumstances under which Li Chi's genuine talent and his ideal class background were especially helpful to him. Poor Mr. Wei, however, was removed from his job and sent back to the commune as a bookkeeper. Li Chi was put in charge of the art department. He had fewer students than before, but those he did have took the course more seriously. For the first time, Li Chi took teaching seriously, and found that he was good at it.

The college authorities also became aware of his ability to teach art, and they began frequently to send him on assignments where the ability had priority. Thus it was, for example, that in early 1962 Li Chi was sent to contribute to the "spare time culture" of the workers in a large metalworking plant near Shanghai.

This was the first time that Li Chi had really been in a factory for any length of time. He hated it. On the rare occasions that the plant was in actual operation, the noise terrified him. Being shut in, away from light and air, in crowded and filthy quarters was the most unpleasant feeling he had ever known.

Even worse perhaps was the life of stultifying boredom that the industrial workers led. The shortages of fuel, power, and raw materials meant that the plant was inoperative most of the time. Nevertheless, three full shifts of workers reported every day, and if they had nothing to do they were given political indoctrination. After their eight-hour shift they had classes in which "culture" and more political indoctrination predominated. Thereafter, they were expected to work at improving themselves in the factory jobs they held and to "innovate," that is, to think up means of raising the efficiency of the plant's production. This was a "leap" factory, which is to say that it was incomplete, hastily thrown together, devoid of any safety devices (which, the workers were told, were aspects of bourgeois degeneracy to be spurned by socialist worker-heroes), and without such effete amenities as recreation facilities, infirmary, or even heating. The workers lived crowded into "red" dormitories under the ever-watchful eyes of the cadres. Even the conversation of the workers was meant to deal only with the "thoughts of Chairman Mao Tse-tung" or with technical matters concerning their jobs. The atmosphere of a strict security prison was unmistakable.

Part of the reason for the prison atmosphere may have been the fact that a surprising number of the workers had been assigned to the factory as punishment for ideological crimes Thus, some were university students or teachers who had "bloomed" inappropriately during the Hundred Flowers. Others had studied at universities in capitalist countries. Still others were guilty of nothing more than the fact that their fathers had been rich.

Even the ordinary workers, however, were of a higher cultural level than the "masses" with whom Li Chi had been in contact. Nevertheless, he was told that he had been brought to the factory only incidentally for cultural purposes. The "innovations" produced by the workers usually needed to be illustrated with at least a simple drawing, but few of the workers were able to present recognizable sketches of their ideas. At first it seemed wholly reasonable to Li Chi that his primary function at the factory was to impart the necessary drawing skill to the workers. He then remembered, however, that what the Communists said was almost always meant to hide the truth. This would indicate that his primary function *was* for "cultural" purposes and only incidentally to teach the workers to draw. With a little discreet questioning he discovered that this indeed was the case.

Apparently, from the time the factory had been built in 1958, the authorities had had difficulty in raising the political level of the proletariat. Left to themselves, the workers seemed to want to spend their spare time with only food, drink, family life, and endless entertainment. It had been easy enough to protect the workers from most of these aspects of bourgeois degeneracy. It had been found, however, that escapist literature (especially in the form of the traditional "fighting stories") had become extremely popular among the workers, even among those who were well educated. The regime had been slow to deprive the masses entirely of their favorite reading material. It could be obtained cheaply enough through peddlers operating in the factory areas if not in the factory canteens themselves, and it was about the only available entertainment. The workers were spending all their spare time reading it. Not only were the stories trash, but they usually made heroes out of men who successfully resisted the lawful authority of the existing regime. Denying the workers access to this type of literature had been no easy task, but soon only good solid Marxist books were available to them.

Thereupon, the workers resorted to gambling, which they carried on feverishly, even sometimes when they should have been working or participating in political discussions. The Western-type cards had been confiscated and publicly burned, and the workers had been lectured ever since on the evils of gambling as a frivolous and nonproductive pastime. Nevertheless, the need to fill the workers' time with more worthwhile effort was recognized, and this was why Li Chi had been brought to the factory. He was expected to keep his classes of workers interested in "art" for long periods each day, and if he happened also to improve the workers' ability to illustrate "innovation" ideas, so much the better.

Li Chi shuddered when he was told all this by the pinched-faced little Party workers who supervised the crowded dormitory where he was given quarters. At that moment Li Chi made two decisions: he would get transferred from the factory as quickly as possible, and he would try to do something that would give the workers a semblance of recreation.

Li Chi thought about these matters for several days. Finally, he chose Mr. Wu, an educated young man who was in one of his classes and who seemed both brighter and bolder than the others. Li Chi asked the young worker to remain after class. "I want to show you," Li Chi said to him, "that art is more than something to bring about cultural uplift; it can also be fun." As he spoke, Li Chi had drawn four large circles, one in each corner of a piece of paper on the easel. Next he put numbers around the inside circumference of the circles in the same places where the numerals of a clock face would be. "Moreover," he went on, "art is not always what it seems to be. For example, I'm willing to gamble that you think these circles are supposed to be four clock faces—" As Li Chi came to the place where the number 11 would be on the clock, he wrote instead "Jack." The twelve was "Queen," and "King" was the center point of the clock, and Li Chi surrounded the word with a diamond shape. He filled in the next circle the same way except that the King was surrounded by the clover design of the playing-card "club" suit. The remaining two circles became "hearts" and "spades."

A light was beginning to dawn in Mr. Wu's eyes, but he said nothing. "Keeping these four clocks in mind," Li Chi continued, "what is the value of this?" In the lower right-hand corner of another piece of paper, in the corner where the spades had been before, Li Chi made a mark.

Wu thought for a moment. "The ten of spades?" he asked.

Li Chi nodded. Then he took his first drawing away and began making little checkmarks in certain positions on another piece of paper. Within minutes, Wu could identify immediately every "card" that Li Chi's mark indicated. The next step was to have Wu mark a blank piece of paper so that Li Chi could identify "cards." Now they had, in effect, an invisible deck. All that remained was to devise a simple gambling game that could be played silently. The one they worked out was similar to "Twenty-one."

Li Chi was standing at the head of the class, and Wu was sitting in the student section. Wordlessly, they played several quick games. "You would have won fifty cents from me," Li Chi said, "but if we were playing in a crowded room, the others would soon guess something of what we were doing."

Thereupon, Li Chi took one of the papers that had on it the marks of one of their games. He studied the paper a moment. Then he used a few interconnecting lines to make a drawing of a village scene. The sketch used, but disguised, the marks of the game.

This game, which later became known as "Innovations Sweepstakes," was generally played only by the educated workers. Wu recruited them carefully, and the gambling game became a daily, but secret, part of Li Chi's classes.

With the help of one of Wu's friends, a former mathematics instructor, Li Chi worked out a simplified version of Mah-Jongg that also could be played with the clock-face number indicators. This game became known as the "Three Red Banners" because each player drew three strokes a turn. It was played by the workers who were literate but less well educated. Finally, for the least educated, a game of complete simplicity was devised.

Li Chi insisted upon strict adherence to three rules. First, those who were let in on the secret of the games had to be chosen with great care to ensure that no one would inform to the cadres. Second, the gambling stakes were low enough so that no one would be seriously hurt by heavy losses. And third, every piece of paper that had been used for games had to be completed with a sketch that was adapted to the strokes that had been used in the games. Because of this last rule, the players soon became clever at disguising their playing sheets, and some inveterate gamblers developed genuine drawing skill.

Inevitably, Li Chi's art classes became exceedingly popular. His classrooms were always filled to capacity, and sometimes his pupils were so fascinated that they went on with their drawing for hours. Morale among the workers increased noticeably.

This, of course, immediately aroused the suspicions of the cadres. Nothing seems to disturb Communists more than the awareness of happy proletarians in the "workers' paradise," and they knew that the workers were up to something forbidden. The "happiness" was quickly traced to Li Chi's class. Li Chi welcomed the first group of cadres who came to investigate his class. He explained to them that one of the most effective ways of stimulating a person's imagination and increasing his drawing skill was to make him finish a sketch that had been started with a few arbitrary fixed lines that had been drawn by someone else. He gave the cadres some of the marked papers and had them try their hand at it. When the cadres compared their efforts with those of the others, they were amazed at the skill Li Chi's students had already developed.

That day, only a few of the boldest "students" had dared to continue gambling under the noses of the cadres, but in the subsequent investigations most of the players went on with their games, at least while others took turns in deliberately distracting the cadres. The authorities soon realized that the workers were engaged in much gambling, and they knew that the gambling was associated with Li Chi's art classes, but they were unable to figure out how it was done. In the discussion-group meetings the authorities constantly introduced the subject of gambling, and always the unanimous opinion of the groups' members was that gambling was an evil of the blackest kind. Suddenly one day Li Chi found that the supply of paper and inks was exhausted and that more was unavailable; old newspapers and pieces of charcoal worked just as well.

Only a day or two later, Li Chi was informed coldly by the factory manager and Party Secretary that his services were no longer required. He was given train fare and asked to return the same day to Wuhu.

Before leaving, however, he had a chance to say goodbye to his friend Wu. "We can't thank you enough for what you've done," Wu said when they were alone at the gate to the factory grounds. "You understand that it isn't the games themselves," he added. "We've learned that we can stick together and that it is possible to fool the cadres—"

One day, more than a year later, Li Chi was one of the judges at an exhibition of "people's art" in Shanghai. With sudden shock he realized that one of the drawings—a sketch of some barges on the Yangtze—was based on the sixteen strokes of four games of "Innovations Sweepstakes," and despite the months between, his trained eye could still pick out the sixteen cards the players had drawn. Li Chi looked closer and saw that the drawing had been made only a few weeks earlier and that it had been done by a worker in a factory many miles away from the one where Li Chi once had had an art class.

Li Chi immediately gave the drawing a first prize, and his comment, which he knew the "artist" would be shown, was: "This drawing reveals much ingenuity. Its technical *innovations* are remarkable, and it is to be hoped that they will *sweep* the country." *

* In Chinese, Li Chi wrote: "This drawing reveals much ingenuity. The technique it uses has never been seen before." The Chinese characters for the words "seen" and "gambling," however, are almost the same. Li Chi made the character look more like the one for "gambling." The artist would understand the message immediately.

目赌 = seen

目赌 = gambling

CHAPTER XIV

👑👑👑👑👑👑👑👑👑👑👑👑👑👑

The Five Good

Chairman Mao, in his early Yenan talks on art, had emphasized that the arts were to "serve" the "peasants, workers, and soldiers." Li Chi, from the viewpoint of his superiors, had done his duty by the first two groups; now it was time for him to take up his soldier-serving obligations. Thus, in about September of 1962, Li Chi found himself visiting a PLA (People's Liberation Army) unit on the Fukien front.

At this time, the Communists had been concerned primarily with the masses of people escaping from the mainland into Hong Kong. Although the flow of refugees now had been stopped, and the subject was not mentioned in the news, it was still an important topic in many of the political discussion groups. The Communists treated the topic according to their own logic. "In the first place," they said in effect, "there was no exodus at all—the whole idea was only slanderous imperialist lies—and in the second place, the exodus was not the fault of the Party. It resulted from the fact that ideological progress had not kept pace with the material advance; in other words, some people simply had been unable to adjust to the unprecedented rise in living standards, and in confusion had foolishly tried to go to Hong Kong."

Nevertheless, in the official media at least, the authorities for the first time were cautiously beginning to admit that, in the past, they had made a few mistakes—the mistakes might have been specified as insignificant and as having been quickly rectified, but the previous pretense of the Party's infallibility was abandoned. It is important to understand that such admissions were only for the record—they were necessary because the gap between the social realities and the official pretenses had become too wide—but no one was expected to discuss them or to admit out loud that they existed. In fact, to ensure that the masses would not get any wrong ideas about who intended, despite a few errors, to continue to hold authority, a new "Five-Anti" campaign was begun.

Nominally, this campaign was against ideological backsliding, but it was peculiar in that the five points varied according to locality, and even to individual discussion groups. For example, in Li Chi's group at the Wuhu Normal College, the Five-Anti campaign was against (1) the two laxities and the six insufficiencies with regard to political activity, (2) the three misconceptions concerning ideological motivation, (3) the nine identifying aspects of bourgeois thinking, (4) the "double two" fallacies concerning (a) the twofold relationship between art and politics and (b) the threefold relationship between art and individualism, and (5) revisionism. Li Chi was unable to name even one detail concerning these "antis." He had recognized that they were mostly just double-talk that Comrade Ho employed to win the approbation of his own superiors. Li Chi therefore had dozed through the actual meetings, but he was fully aware that the entire nation was engaged in the new campaign. Thus he expected the soldiers with whom he was billeted to be exhorting each other to eschew five evils pertinent to the military profession.

To Li Chi's surprise and confusion, however, the soldiers, instead of discussing five evils, were industriously concerned with the "Five Good." Moreover, they obviously had been engaged in their campaign for some time; every soldier knew what the Five Good were, and needed to refer to each one only by its appropriate number. All Li Chi could gather from the conversations was that every soldier in the unit wanted to be credited with the Five Good in order that he could belong to a Four-Good company. The sudden unexpected switch in dealing with vices and then virtues was not easy to make and probably was responsible for the trouble in which Li Chi soon found himself.

The morning Li Chi arrived at the military installation he reported to the office of a battalion commander; here, he was referred to the office of Comrade Cheng, the battalion's political officer, who happened to be out. Li Chi therefore was received by the officer's deputy, Comrade Hua, who expressed both delight and relief at seeing Li Chi. He took Li Chi at once to an exhibition of paintings and drawings that the soldiers had done. It was Li Chi's duty to judge the artwork, but he quickly perceived that his judgment was meant to be based, not on the skill of a particular soldier-artist, but on the soldier's rating in the Five Good. Comrade Hua therefore made the decisions about which pictures rated commendation, and Li Chi merely confirmed them. Li Chi did not mind in the least; he knew that the soldier-artists expected to be rated politically rather than artistically and probably would have been surprised by any other arrangement. Li Chi was surprised by the fact that every one of the soldiers' pictures was on the subject of peaceful fishermen.

Judging the exhibition took no more than three hours. When the task was finished, Li Chi asked Comrade Hua what other tasks would be expected of him during his visit with the unit. Comrade Hua appeared astonished. "We were simply told to expect you," he said. "We naturally assumed you'd tell *us* what you wanted."

"I was told to *serve* you," Li Chi said.

"We'll be glad to serve *you* in any way we can," Hua replied. "Tell us what you want, and we'll get it for you."

Li Chi could think of nothing at the moment. He was turned over to the platoon with which he was billeted. He joined these men just in time to attend their discussion-group meeting. It was here that he first learned how seriously the men took the Four and the Five Good. When the meeting was over, he drew the platoon leader aside. "I am to set up my own project here, and perhaps you can help me," Li Chi said. "Can you suggest anyone whose portrait I might paint?"

The man considered, frowning. Then he brightened and struck his palm with his fist. "Soldier Ying!" he exclaimed. "During the Korean War, Ying's life was saved by a copy of Chairman Mao's writings." The platoon leader struck a dramatic pose. " 'Chairman Mao's writings and my rifle are my most prized possessions,' " he said, quoting, apparently, Soldier Ying. " 'They are all I need for my everlasting protection.' "

"Good," Li Chi said. "Where can I find Soldier Ying?"

The platoon leader closed his eyes and drew a deep shuddering breath. "Soldier Ying died the valorous death of a people's hero," he said sonorously, and added, "No book is big enough to protect a man from every bullet."

Li Chi could not deny this piece of military wisdom, and therefore changed the subject. "Then maybe you could recommend one of the men whose Five Good is the best," he said.

The platoon leader glowered at Li Chi and began to breathe heavily again. "I warn you not to make fun of us," he said shakily. "No one in our company—in fact no one in the battalion, or even in the regiment—has been acclaimed a Five-Good soldier."

Li Chi hastened to apologize and to state that he had not meant to be disparaging. "I had not realized that the Five Good were so difficult to achieve," he said, adding, "You must tell me what they are."

"Gladly!" the platoon leader said. "The first is 'good in political ideology.' " He snapped to attention and shot up his fist in a Communist salute. "The Chinese Communist Party: eternal leadership of the Chinese people. Chairman Mao Tse-tung: greatest genius and truest inspiration of the people. The Three Red Banners . . ." He screwed up his face in the effort to think, but evidently he had forgotten his catechism

"What is the second Good?" Li Chi asked.

The man dropped to one knee, took aim with an imaginary rifle, and drilled Li Chi between the eyes. Then he flung himself behind a chair and at the same time lobbed an imaginary grenade at Li Chi with deadly accuracy. Next, he leaped onto a chair and sprayed Li Chi with imaginary submachine-gun fire. Finally he charged, his face hideously ferocious, and speared Li Chi's quivering remains with an imaginary bayonet. "Good at military techniques is the second," he said.

"And the third?" Li Chi asked.

"Good at Chairman Mao's Three-Eight style," the platoon leader said, and seeing that Li Chi did not remember them, he went to the blackboard and began to write out the characters for the three phrases. Unfortunately, he was unable to finish them. An enormous soldier appeared, seemingly from nowhere, and seized the platoon leader from behind.

"I earn Five Good," the soldier said. "I get 'Three-Alert' award. Orders are 'Keep alert to spoken word, to written character, and to meaningful look or gesture that tell secrets to strangers.' You break all three."

Despite the platoon leader's curses, protests, and threats, he was carried away, and Li Chi was left alone.

Subsequently, Li Chi learned that according to a strict security regulation, when a stranger was in camp nothing should be written down that the stranger could see. Whether or not this applied to the glorious and immortal words of Chairman Mao was the subject of some argument. In the end, the platoon leader had not been punished, but he had been given a severe reprimand.

173

Li Chi should have seen through this situation and profited from it; considering the example of the platoon leader, what Li Chi did was inexcusably careless. Not having any definitely assigned project other than to "serve" the soldiers, Li Chi decided to submit a large canvas on which something of a soldier's life was depicted. He therefore spent a few days wandering around the camp making sketches of various soldiers engaged in typical activities: working, drilling, loafing, talking, sleeping, reading, and listening to lectures. It was inevitable that the men would begin to ask each other who the stranger was who snooped into and recorded everything. Eventually, some superactivist working hard toward a Five Good was sure to decide that Li Chi must be just the sort of person against whom all the elaborate security precautions were designed.

Nevertheless, Li Chi had filled his notebook with sketches, had transferred the sketches to the big canvas, and had begun to paint before he was suddenly surrounded by armed soldiers and seized from behind. Immediately, Li Chi understood that he had blundered and that from the military viewpoint he had committed a serious breach of security. He therefore went along without protesting, although the men who arrested him were disturbingly grim and silent. He was locked in a small room with two armed guards standing over him. One of the guards was the platoon leader to whom Li Chi had spoken originally.

"What will they do to me?" Li Chi asked the man.

"What we always do to counterrevolutionaries and imperialist agents," the platoon leader replied. Thereupon, he put down his rifle and enacted an execution, playing graphically both the part of the executed and the executioner. Li Chi was aware of a strong feeling of uneasiness, but he told himself that it was absurd; since the threat of invasion from Taiwan, the PLA was expected to be especially alert, and it was therefore reasonable that he should be investigated thoroughly. Soon, however, the authorities would find that his bona fides were entirely in order.

His guards were changed frequently, but the next day the pair that had included the platoon leader returned to the duty. "What do you think I ought to do?" Li Chi asked the man.

The platoon leader jerked up his rifle and pointed it at Li Chi. "Don't talk to me, you spy," he said. "We have had strict orders to say nothing to you, and no one whom Battalion Political Officer Cheng has declared a paid imperialist agent and an enemy of the people is going to get any information out of me."

A dim light in Li Chi's memory began slowly to brighten. "Comrade Cheng!" he exclaimed. "Is he a short husky man with a thick nose and pockmarks?"

The platoon leader snorted contemptuously. "The fact that you obviously know Comrade Cheng is immaterial," he said. "What is important is that he knows *you*. He knows you so-called artists and he has tracked you down. He got you here where he could keep you under expert observation until you gave yourself away."

Everything now came back to Li Chi, and he groaned. Comrade Cheng had been the big semiliterate Party Secretary at the Art Institute—Comrade Cheng and (who was the other one? Tan, Comrade Tan)—six years ago, during the Hundred Flowers. Li Chi had "blossomed" then by pitting Cheng and Tan against each other so that both "weeds" had been torn up from their posts. Cheng was the one who approved of art so long as it depicted the bloodier aspects of "socialist action." Apparently he had been transferred from his easy post at the Art Institute to this much more rugged one of battalion political officer; it had taken all these years for his slow brain to figure out what had happened and who was responsible for it. Now Comrade Cheng was moving equally methodically in seeking revenge. Li Chi was really frightened.

Days passed, and still Li Chi was guarded but not questioned. He understood that every detail of his past was being scrutinized for evidence that could be used against him. He knew that his record was reasonably clean and that the long wait indicated difficulty in uncovering incriminating evidence. He hoped that this would strengthen his position, but he knew that the authorities would have no scruple about introducing false evidence if they really wanted a conviction. His one slight advantage was in the fact that he knew Comrade Cheng was working against him. Everyday, Li Chi questioned the platoon leader, who, in refusing to answer, talked so much that Li Chi often wished the man would shut up. Li Chi filled his notebook with notes.

Finally the waiting and worrying were over. He was taken suddenly from his cell one morning to a large office in a distant part of the camp. From a sign he realized that his hearing was being held in the office of the regimental commander. Among the officials, Li Chi recognized Comrade Cheng immediately, and the man's look of sheer hatred provided immediate proof that he was indeed Li Chi's enemy. The regimental commander and political officer were men of a type similar to Comrade Cheng, and Li Chi could read no sympathy in their hard faces. Li Chi's incompleted painting was displayed on the wall.

Comrade Cheng began at once an all-out attack. He reminded the other officials that he had been the Party Secretary of the Peking Art Institute and that he therefore could be expected to know the difference between art for art's sake and art for some ulterior motive. "That picture," he shouted, "is the work of a spy!" He then pointed out how the enemy could determine the armament, equipment, battle readiness, and other vital intelligence factors of the PLA's basic fighting unit just from studying the picture. He submitted that Li Chi intended to photograph the picture when he had finished it and send the photo to his foreign masters. Thereupon, Cheng began an attack upon Li Chi himself. Some parts of the attack twisted facts about Li Chi's past or planted innuendos concerning his behavior. Most of it, however, was a plea not to consider the seeming innocence of Li Chi's record; the argument was that the imperialist were sure to pick their agents only among those whose records were clean.

Cheng ended his attack by reminding the officials that no unit in the regiment, or even in the division, had been honored with a Four-Good citation. Perhaps, he suggested, by doing their duty in this grave security matter, the proper authorities would finally extend to their unit the recognition it deserved. Li Chi realized instantly that this was the argument that had the most effect. The officials murmured among themselves and looked at Li Chi with cold eyes. These men had no feelings of sympathy or compassion. They understood nothing about art, and cared even less for it or for artists. They could save themselves time and effort, they could give their comrade Cheng the personal satisfaction he seemed to desire so much, and they could put themselves in a position of possibly receiving high commendation—and all they had to do was to agree to the disposal of a worthless artist and his worthless picture.

This was what Li Chi had to fight. He suppressed his panic and made himself think. He decided that this was no time for subtleties or half measures. "The comrade battalion political officer is to be commended for his conscientiousness in regard to the important matter of security," he said, "but he knows nothing about pictures. It was because of this fact that he was removed from his post at the Art Institute."

These words caused a gasp of astonishment among his listeners, and even Cheng seemed too shocked to be offended. Outright criticism of a Party official by one of the masses—that is, by one who did not even belong to the Party—was unheard of. The effect was to make Li Chi seem superbly confident in the strength of his position. The officials looked at him with new interest as he told them he would explain his painting to them so that they could judge its value.

He began by handing his notebook to the regimental commander and requesting that the man read from it the title that Li Chi had selected for the painting and that would be put on the completed work: "Five-Good Men of a Four-Good Company Practice the Four Togethernesses and the Four Relationships Which, When Accompanied by the Four Criteria of Action and the Three Alerts, Enable the Men to Walk on Two Legs to Achieve the Four Firsts in Socialist Progress Under the Three Red Banners."

In the silence that followed, Li Chi picked up a ruler and went to his painting. "The Five Good," he said, "good in political and ideological thinking, in Chairman Mao's Three-Eight style, in military training, in discipline, and in physical fitness are illustrated here, here, and here." Li Chi pointed with his ruler. "The work, live, meet danger and die together of the Four Togethernesses are depicted here," Li Chi continued, pointing to other parts of the painting. "The Four Relationships between men and weapons, between ordinary work and political work, between ideological and routine work within political work, and between book thoughts and living thoughts are depicted in these drawings. Notice how the Four Firsts that have priority in these relationships are indicated. And finally, you see here the glorious Three Red Banners symbolizing the General Line, the Great Leap Forward, and the People's Communes, protected by the Three Alerts."

Li Chi paused while the slower military minds absorbed all this political indoctrination.

"I might add that this painting also is indicative of the Five Goods for an artist," Li Chi said. "Good in ideological content, in political motivation, in serving the masses, in socialist realism, and in artistic technique." Li Chi regarded his listeners with something almost like disdain. "Admittedly the political level in Peking, where this picture will be shown, is infinitely higher than it is here, so that all that I have pointed out to you will be fully and immediately apparent to everyone there." He looked around at his silent listeners. "And what will be the reaction of the Peking officials, including our beloved Chairman Mao Tse-tung? First, as a people's artist, dedicated to socialist realism, they will know that what I have pictured is pure truth. And what is the truth I have shown? I have illustrated the men

178

from a certain unit engaged in the activities that entitle them to the Five-Good award and their unit the Four-Good citation. Inevitably, it will be discovered that through some oversight the unit that so richly deserves these honors has not actually received them." Li Chi returned to his chair, but before he sat down he made his final statement. "Which do you think is the most likely to bring honor and citation to this unit?" he asked. "The notoriety you receive from destroying a famous people's artist and a masterpiece of socialist realism, or letting this painting spread loudly and clearly the truth of its message to the very highest authorities in our country?"

Thereafter Li Chi waited alone in an outer office for the longest fifteen minutes of his life. When he was recalled, however, the regimental commander thanked him for having given them all an inspiring lesson in political action. Li Chi was begged to continue the painting * and to finish it without further delay.

Comrade Cheng sat silently and with lowered head. The next day he was gone, and Li Chi never saw him again.

* No real painting similar to this one has been described in the press, to the best of my knowledge. Nevertheless, other variations of this story mention a widely publicized hoax that was perpetrated in late 1964. On the cover of the final 1964 issue of the magazine *China Youth* was the reproduction of an oil painting entitled "You Go Ahead, I'll Follow." It showed commune workers picking cotton. In the tangled cotton stalks, however, a close look revealed the features of Mao Tse-tung and Lenin being trampled underfoot. In the background, a group of workers was depicted carrying the "Three Red Banners"; the carrier of the second banner (the one representing the Great Leap Forward) could be seen stumbling so that his banner dragged in the dust. These aspects of the painting had been missed by the censors. When the hoax was discovered, the regime lost much face, and the leaders reacted with customary dudgeon. The accredited artist was named Li Tse-hou, and apparently he took the brunt of the official fury. Although this type of hoax is traditional in China, it is untypical of Li Chi, and I therefore did not associate him with it.

CHAPTER XV

Lei Feng

In 1963 Li Chi was twenty-four. He had not seen his parents for ten years. He missed them and he decided that he owed himself a visit to them. His funds were inadequate for such a holiday, however, and the Communists had no sympathy whatever for the sentiments that bound family members together. Li Chi, therefore, was forced to resort to subterfuge.

The Wuhu Normal College faculty members were obligated to do a month of manual labor each year. Invariably, Comrade Ho managed to satisfy this requirement for his group with some absurdly easy tasks. One of the main slogans of the period, however, was still "all out for agriculture." Seemingly from a rush of patriotism to the head, Li Chi demanded permission to "serve agriculture" for his 1963 month of manual labor. The college authorities were astounded. Here was a *voluntary* voluntary request. Before they quite knew what they were doing, they had granted him the permission; they had assigned him to the commune (and even to the particular production team) he had specified, and, as was customary, they had given him the necessary funds for traveling expenses. What is more, Li Chi, whom Comrade Ho and his discussion-group members had long labeled an "unregenerate backward element," was now complimented for his "high ideological level" and his "progressiveness" by the college president and Party Secretary.

Naturally, the commune Li Chi had stipulated was the one in which his parents lived; he had had himself assigned to the production team on which his father and older brother worked. For all practical purposes, therefore, Li Chi's joyous family reunion was provided for him with the compliments of the People's Government. Li Chi made the occasion even more festive by turning over his month's ration coupons to his parents, thereby assuring a slightly improved diet for everyone. Even better, he told his father and brother that he would turn back the work points he earned on the production team to be divided among the production-team members. In return he was assured that he would be required to make only a token effort to earn his work points and that he could spend his time as he chose. Li Chi looked forward to a month of pleasant leisure.

On the first evening of his homecoming, relatives, neighbors, and other team members came with their families to welcome him back. His parents' hut was crowded. Li Chi perceived that these people were awed by his achievements but that, when they found him to be simple, unaffected, and friendly, they responded with warm affection as well. As the evening progressed, however, Li Chi was aware of an undercurrent of tension, as though each person there endured his own private despair.

Most of the evening he was followed about by his three-year-old niece. She appeared immediately whenever he sat down. She would prop herself against his knee, her finger in her mouth, and stare up at him with big worshipful eyes.

Finally he asked her, "Well, what do you think of your uncle Li Chi?"

She took the finger reluctantly from her mouth. "I think you are ugly like a monkey," she said sweetly, "but I love you." With that she scrambled into his lap.

The child's mother, who was Li Chi's brother's wife, was horrified and embarrassed, but all the others laughed. While everyone was off guard, Li Chi asked them suddenly and bluntly what it was that bothered them all.

The laughter stopped abruptly. The guests glanced at one another or looked at their feet, but no one answered. Finally, Team Leader Liang Shih-hua stepped forward; he murmured polite excuses, and then left. When he was gone, Li Chi saw that the others relaxed a little. Li Chi was sorry, because he had immediately liked the intelligent young Liang.

"Surely," he said, "the team leader does not make things difficult for you?"

His brother shrugged. "Basically, Liang is all right, but he's a Youth League member. He doesn't know whether he's on our side or on the side of the comrades."

"Even so," Li Chi's father said, "he would make a better Party cadre for the village than any we've had so far—especially the present one."

This comment caused a murmur of approval from the others.

"Then it's the cadre that bothers you," Li Chi said.

"I didn't say that," his brother said hastily.

"No, but you meant it," Li Chi said. "What does he do? Is he unjust? Does he 'squeeze'?" Li Chi realized quickly that his questions had brought out actual fear within the others.

"The corrupt cadres give us little trouble," his brother said finally. "At least we get *something* in return for the graft we pay."

"I'll give you an example," his father said suddenly. "We wanted some wine to celebrate your homecoming, and the cadre promised to get it for us. We took up a collection and gave it to him. What did he do with it? He sent it to Mao Tse-tung along with a letter in our name. He cheated us."

"No, that's not right," a cousin of Li Chi's said. "He lied to us to get our money, yes, but he included some of his own in the donation. It was that he didn't consult us about it. And that letter he wrote and signed our names to, it made us sound so ignorant, so stupid—"

Someone else spoke up. "He made the children give up their games period at school and 'contribute' it to 'socialist construction.' He doesn't believe children should play—only work."

This seemed to encourage the others to speak out their complaints against the hated cadre. Li Chi recognized the cadre's type: the dehumanized Party worker who operated solely from a set of dogmatic slogans rather than from any understanding of, or sympathy for, human beings. What dismayed Li Chi was that his people had not learned how to cope with the type. Suddenly, the people became frightened at their own indiscretions, and the conversation stopped.

Li Chi looked down at his niece who still sat in his lap. "Do you know what we've been talking about, little one?" he asked her.

She nodded and wriggled happily at having his attention. "The village cadre, Comrade Tzu," she said, and added innocently, "I hate his guts."

Li Chi determined that, if he possibly could, he would do something about the cadre. Hoping for inspiration on the subject, the next afternoon he attended a discussion-group meeting over which Comrade Tzu presided. The man looked precisely as Li Chi had imagined him: an undersized, pinch-faced, unimaginative, and humorless fanatic. The only characteristic that made him even slightly different from the whole breed of cadre was the fact that Comrade Tzu was a dapper little man; his Communist uniform was threadbare but meticulously clean, and he had a scrubbed look as though he had just stepped from a bath.

The meeting was nothing like the ones Li Chi was used to. Comrade Tzu did not bother with the pretense that he was con-

183

ducting a democratic forum in which the "will of the masses" was expressed. He harangued his listeners for almost three hours. He made no effort to disguise in his rasping voice the contempt he felt for his audience, and he talked down to them as though they were half-witted children. At one point, he condemned them for allowing their "brats" to play in the streets of the village; this was too much—it had been he who forced the children to give up their play period at school—and the audience snarled its anger and hatred. To Li Chi's amazement, Comrade Tzu snarled back at his audience; he shouted the people down; he cursed, threatened, and shook his fists at them until they cowered under the fury of his abuse. Despite himself, Li Chi was impressed at the power and courage of this hateful little man. Later that evening, in bed in the dark, Li Chi made himself stay awake. In his mind he went over everything the cadre had said.

The cadre's sermon had been on the subject of Lei Feng. During 1963, in Communist China, the chief topics within the political discussion groups were the evils of Russian deviationism and the virtues of certain Chinese Communist heroes. Of these heroes, the favorite was a man called Lei Feng who had died shortly before at a young age while serving with an army motor transport company. Despite his short life, however, he had served agriculture and industry as well as the army. He had the ideal proletarian background. He had suffered horribly under the old regime and had lived blissfully in the new regime. Although he was barely literate, he had written a voluminous diary in the style typical of a propaganda cadre, and it just so happened that an incredible number of photographs illustrating every aspect of his life and activities had been taken.

Lei Feng's chronic cheerfulness and his energy, according to the publicity, were phenomenal. When taking a train trip, he would carry the luggage of the other passengers, find seats for the aged, and help mothers with their children; under way, he would read newspapers aloud for everyone and then deliver lectures on the glorious deeds of the noble Party cadres. That finished, he would scrub the floor of the train. On a picnic with friends, he would pretend to a stomachache, divide his food among the others, and then lecture them about the policies of the Party. Often he would get up at night and wash the socks and underwear of his companions. Whatever money he earned always went to the "needy"; invariably every pay day he was overpaid, owing to clerical errors, and he would go through the most excruciating suffering in order to return the unearned portion. He practiced thrift to an extravagant degree. For example, he had found the toothbrush he used in a trash pile; he had trimmed off the stained ends of the bristle, washed what remained carefully, and claimed it was "just as good as new." He was an inveterate collector of junk, which, in his case, always turned out to be miraculously useful. An endless stream of stories and articles, glorifying Lei Feng, filled the press. Even Li Chi, the previous March, had been pressured into painting an idealized portrait of him. It was typical of a cadre like Tzu really to believe that he was so wise and his listeners were so stupid that he could arouse in them a genuine desire to emulate Lei Feng. He succeeded, of course, only in making them loathe Lei Feng—and him—even more.

The next morning Li Chi still had no idea about what could be done with Comrade Tzu, but he did have definite opinions concerning Comrade Liang Shih-hua, the production team leader. Li Chi had been given a hoe with which to weed a section of ripening grain field, and he worked his row in such a way that he could come close to the team leader out of hearing of the others. "I want to speak to you—alone," he said sternly to Liang; the young man looked up at him in surprise, but Li Chi said, "Go at once behind that wall. I'll join you in a minute."

When they were out of sight as well as out of hearing, Li Chi stared at the young man coldly for a moment and then said, "The other night at my parents' house, I want to know why you left early." This question obviously was so unexpected and so embarrassing to the young man that he could only stammer incoherently. "I *know* why you left," Li Chi interrupted him to say, "but I want you to say it out loud—so you can hear it as well as I."

The young man stiffened, and his eyes flashed angrily at Li Chi. "You had asked our people what was bothering them. I knew what it was. I knew that no one would answer you while I was there."

"Why wouldn't our people answer me while you were there?" Li Chi demanded.

"Because they thought I might betray them," Liang said, his voice trembling as though he were fighting down sobs.

"And are they not right to distrust you?" Li Chi asked.

At this, tears did stream down the young man's cheeks. "What can I do?" he pleaded. "I've tried to help. They'll never know how often I've interceded on their behalf."

Li Chi forced himself to remain cold and unsympathetic. "And every time you interceded on behalf of our people, you made the cadres angry with you. Isn't that right? And every time you did what the cadres wanted, our people suffered."

"I'm in the middle," Liang cried, "no matter what I do, it's wrong."

Liang sobbed now, uncontrollably. Li Chi waited until the young man calmed himself. "You understand that you must make a decision right now," Li Chi said then. "You cannot put it off any longer. Do you belong to us or to *them?*" Li Chi put his hands on the young man's shoulders and shook him. "It's not really a decision. You belong to us, and to no one else. When Comrade Tzu took the wine money for my homecoming celebration, he cheated our people, didn't he?" Liang nodded, and Li Chi continued: "From the beginning, the cadres have cheated and lied to our people, have they not?"

Liang sighed deeply and his shoulders slumped, but he nodded.

"Well, then," Li Chi continued, "it's time you faced what

you're going to do about it." He allowed himself now to grin at the young man. "You will have to play two parts. You must convince the Communists you're on their side *against* us, but you must never forget, even for a moment, that you're on our side against them."

Liang looked at Li Chi questioningly. "I'd never get away with it," he said.

"You'll be amazed at what you can do if your life depends on it," Li Chi said calmly. "Once you have Comrade Tzu's job, there are thousands of ways you can help our people, relieve their suffering, protect them, make things easier for them—"

Liang now looked at Li Chi in amazement. "Tzu's job!" he exclaimed. "But they would never give it to me. They always bring in an outsider."

"Only because they've never been able to trust one of us to work entirely for their interests rather than for ours," Li Chi said. "Tzu's only advantage to them is that he hates us; this assures his loyalty, but he is a city man who does not understand peasant problems. Thus he is not efficient in dealing with us. The comrades know you could do a much better job and they would prefer you, if they thought you could be trusted." A light of understanding came into Liang's eyes, and Li Chi added, "I will give you one week to convince Comrade Tzu that you ought to be made a Party member."

There was silence while Liang thought over the matter. "I suppose once Tzu accepted me and designated me his successor here, you'd move to have Tzu kicked out."

Li Chi shrugged. "Something like that."

"That's easy enough," Liang continued. "We've done it before with unpopular cadres. Everyone simply refuses to cooperate with him. The authorities take him away all right, but they retaliate on us brutally—and I'd be expected to punish my own people."

"More than anything else, the Communists fear *united* opposition, and they always move ruthlessly against it," Li Chi said.

"If we are to discredit Tzu, we must do it in such a way that no one will think it was planned by a group—"

Thereupon, Li Chi made Liang tell everything he knew about the cadre. Li Chi learned that Tzu had been born and raised in Shanghai. He had been a Party cadre in one of the factories. After the Great Leap, the factory had been able to operate at only a small percentage of its capacity. Tzu was one of the excess employees who were sent to "serve agriculture." Like many urban dwellers, he loathed the countryside and the peasants. He was embittered by the blow he had received from Fate. "He takes it out on us by driving us like animals, but he drives himself even harder."

"Still, he must have some weakness," Li Chi said.

Liang shook his head. He leaned over and picked up the hoe Li Chi had been using. "Look at this," Liang said. "It was made in Tzu's old factory which was converted to 'serve agriculture.' We got thousands of them a couple of years ago, but they broke the first time they were used." Li Chi saw now that the neckpiece of the hoe was curved in an unusual way, apparently in the attempt to save metal. The faulty design plus the poor quality of steel meant that the implement was virtually useless, because even soldering the break would not overcome the basic defect. Nevertheless, the defect had been cleverly corrected by nothing more than a small piece of wood carved to fit the curve and held in place by two small bits of wire. "With that piece of wood, the hoe is practically indestructible," Liang said, "and Tzu has set himself the task of fixing every single one of those hoes himself—he says it's his 'Lei Feng emulation' contribution. The way to correct the hoe's defect seems obvious now, but I don't think it would have occurred to anyone here."

"Hmmm," Li Chi said. "I'll bet it would never have occurred to anyone at the factory, either. In fact, I'll bet that no one has ever dared to tell the factory that their hoes were defective."

"Sir, if you have some plan in mind I do not think you ought to tell me," Liang said.

Li Chi nodded. "You can tell Tzu that you've told the peasants to heed his words about emulating Lei Feng and that you've ordered the children to be kept out of the way by being given lessons in Lei Feng's deeds."

Liang nodded. Li Chi shook his hand, and turned to leave. "One more thing," Liang said. "I want to thank you, sir, for showing me what I had to do—"

That evening, in his father's house, Li Chi had a long, quiet conference with the other team members. He learned that, twelve days hence, the village was to be inspected by the top commune authorities. Actually, since the middle of 1961, the communes had existed only on paper. At the most, the production brigade "owned" the land, property, and equipment of the agricultural unit, but in actual practice now the small production teams that made up a brigade operated on their own authority. The face-saving pretense that the commune administrative structure still existed was maintained by gestures such as the inspection. In Li Chi's plan, the move against Comrade Tzu would begin nine days hence, three days before the inspection.

Later still that same night, Li Chi wrote a letter to the manager of the Shanghai factory. He did not say what his position was or describe it in any way. Nevertheless, he duplicated perfectly the arrogant, curt, and slightly crude writing style that invariably identified a high Party official. The reader therefore could not be blamed for assuming that Li Chi was one of the top officials of the commune. The letter began by saying bluntly that the hoes received from the factory had been defective and useless—this alone was enough to prove the rank of the writer. Nevertheless, Li Chi wrote, the defect had been corrected and the hoes made usable by a simple, inexpensive, and wholly effective device that had originated from an erstwhile employee of the factory, Comrade Tzu. Li Chi drew an excellent sketch of the device. He then pointed out that the commune people, being agriculturally minded, were not impressed with Tzu's achievement—they had merely obtained finally what they should have had in the first place. The factory people, however, ought to be extremely grateful for Tzu's contribution. Li Chi suggested that a man of Tzu's mechanical ability would make a far greater contribution to socialist construction in the hoe factory than in a commune, and he implied that if the factory authorities did not rehire Comrade Tzu at once, they would be guilty of criminal negligence. Finally, he suggested that they obtain the necessary transfer authorization and address the necessary correspondence to Comrade Tzu but that they should mail the paper to him, Li Chi, who, no doubt, would be able to "expedite the matter."

As Li Chi suspected, no one had ever dared to tell the factory people that their hoes were defective. Eight days later, he received their reply. They were crushed and terrified. They assumed that Li Chi was a high official who was writing to them unofficially in order to keep their colossal blunder off the record. Thus they were maudlinly grateful, and they readily accepted the suggestion that Comrade Tzu should be rehired. In fact, with the practical knowledge he had obtained, he should be more useful now than before, and they were prepared to offer him a more responsible position. The necessary papers were enclosed. Li Chi smiled and put the papers away.

Just before dawn the next morning, the children of the village began to "apply the lesson of Lei Feng." They started with a parade back and forth along the one street of the village, shouting the Lei Feng slogans at the tops of their voices. They tended to save their noisiest clamor to dispense in the vicinity of Comrade Tzu's hut. He came to the door, his face red with anger, but he could hardly ask the children to stop what he had been exhorting their parents to have them do. When the men left for the fields, the children ceased their shouting and a merciful silence descended upon the village—for a few minutes.

The children now broke up into teams, each with obviously preassigned tasks. One group, for example, collected every trunk and large container in the village; these were placed in the schoolroom, which was also used for the discussion-group meetings. The containers were filled with trash and were labeled in childish characters from the Lei Feng quotations concerning "never throwing anything away." The bits of string, broken glass, or rusty metal that always proved so useful to Lei Feng seemed now to make only a mess.

An even worse mess was made by the fertilizer-collecting group. Lei Feng apparently was never so happy as when he was carrying full pails of rich fertilizer from the latrines to the fields, and now his little imitators sang gay patriotic songs as they piled the reeking contents of their pails in the open space near Comrade Tzu's hut. Chairman Mao Tse-tung himself had said that the good ripe "revolutionary" smell of the masses was like perfume to him, and Comrade Tzu, therefore, was also sure to enjoy it.

When this task had been finished and the children themselves were especially rich with the revolutionary odor, they burst into Comrade Tzu's room and began to clean it. Admittedly their spirit was more to be commended than their proficiency, and the truth is that they made the room worse than it was before. Comrade Tzu was distracted from this matter, however, by another proud little group of reeking youngsters who showed him his underwear and socks that they had washed. According to witnesses, he had chased the children, but his howling had been drowned in a renewed shouting of slogans from the children. Upon returning to his room, no one saw his reaction to what other children had done in his absence. For the trash collection, the children had taken his trunk, having dumped its contents on the dirt floor. Comrade Tzu's other pair of pants (few people in the village could boast of two pairs, and the children could be forgiven their ignorance in believing that a person was meant to have only one pair) were given to old Mr. Hsi, who was bedridden and who had no pants at all. Whatever Tzu's reaction, the children paid no attention to it. Instead of playing games, they spent their time helping the village cadre in every ingenious way that their unfettered imaginations could devise.

When the men came home from the fields, their bellows of outrage and indignation could be heard from one end of the village to the other. Li Chi had insisted that each one of them should appear to suffer at least as badly as, if not worse than, Comrade Tzu from the children's emulation campaign.

By evening, Li Chi could not contain his curiosity any longer and he went in search of the cadre. Li Chi found him in the shed where the community tools were stored. The cadre was engaged in the repair of the defective hoes. He was so absorbed in his work that he did not hear Li Chi enter. Li Chi watched the nimble fingers working, and he saw that the look on the man's face was almost happy.

The look changed immediately when he saw Li Chi. "Don't worry," Li Chi said to him. "I'm not going to emulate Lei Feng."

The cadre got slowly to his feet. "So you're behind all this! I should have known. You're one of them, and an intellectual as well," he said. He was visibly growing angrier. "But you'll be sorry. All of you. I'll make you pay—"

"Calm down, Comrade," Li Chi said. He leaned against the door and lighted a cigarette. "It was you who started this Lei Feng mess, and you have only yourself to blame."

Comrade Tzu was so astonished to be talked to in this manner by one of the masses that he could only sputter, incoherent in his rage.

"Subconsciously, however, the children's actions today indicate that you are not popular here," Li Chi continued. "I've come to offer you a bargain. I'll see to it that you get transferred back to Shanghai, in fact back to the same factory you used to work in. You, however, must arrange it so that Comrade Liang Shih-hua will take your place."

Comrade Tzu's mouth fell open in shocked surprise. Li Chi

saw that even the mention of the factory and of Shanghai brought a gleam of life into the cadre's eyes. It faded quickly, however, into disbelief and then to anger again. "You dare to bargain with me?" he said. "You counterrevolutionary, you *intellectual!* I'll have you shot."

Li Chi shrugged. "Take care," he said. "You are unpopular here, and it would be your word against mine."

"The word of a Party member against one of the masses—an *intellectual,*" Tzu said, and he made the word sound like a curse.

"You'd better wait until after the inspection before you do anything rash," Li Chi said.

This jolted the cadre. "Get out!" he said.

Li Chi turned and left. Outside, across the street, his father was standing. Li Chi nodded at him. His father nodded back, and the two men strolled off in opposite directions. The next morning, the day before the inspections, Comrade Tzu had arranged for a trial run. The pretense was maintained that the inspector would pick at random the houses he would visit, but of course the whole little drama was carefully staged. The chosen families were permitted to stay home from the fields.

The first family Tzu called upon, however, seemed to be genuinely surprised by the visit. They were only half dressed, and their room was in filthy disorder. The couple stood with the sullen, beaten look of half-starved people. They cringed when Tzu shouted at them, but otherwise they reacted with complete apathy to his threats. Tzu left, slamming the door.

In the next hut, the situation was reversed. The room here was immaculate. There was every indication of prosperity. The family members were well fed and jovial. In fact, the husky head of the house was so friendly and intimate with Tzu that he actually put his arm around the cadre's shoulders.

The people in the next house also showed signs of prosperity. Here, however, the two attractive daughters demonstrated easy familiarity with Tzu—but not too much; their attitude, when combined with the father's sullen expression, fairly shouted Tzu's depravity.

In the next house, the people were like the first: beaten, apathetic, and starved. Tzu was silent now, but he went doggedly from house to house. By the end of the tour it was apparent that any accompanying inspector would have had the unmistakable impression that Tzu was the most corrupt and degenerate member the Party had. No one would possibly believe that the peasants were capable of such subtle acting and of such an elaborately contrived plan.

Li Chi was waiting for the cadre. He saw that the little man was pale and shaking. "All right," Tzu said, "what is it you want?"

"I told you," Li Chi said. "Tomorrow morning when the officials arrive, you tell them you might be leaving soon, and you get from them in writing their authorization for Liang to take your place."

"And where will I be going?" Tzu asked. There were cynicism and resignation in his voice.

"Get that authorization," Li Chi said, "and you'll find that these people will act quite differently tomorrow—and you'll be on your way back to your old job in Shanghai before the week is over."

Once again the momentary light came into the cadre's eyes at the mention of Shanghai and his old job. "You're lying," he said dully. "You must be—you couldn't do anything about it."

"I'm not lying," Li Chi replied. "What you saw today was lying and cheating. It's the sort of thing we masses learn from you and the Party. But I promise you I'm telling the truth."

Tzu looked at him as though seeing him for the first time. "What you ask for is not particularly difficult," he said. "If I were really leaving, I might well recommend Liang as my own choice."

Li Chi realized with satisfaction that Liang must have worked hard at convincing the cadre that his loyalty was solely to the Party. Nevertheless, for Tzu, he only shrugged. "How we get along with Liang when he takes your place is our problem," he said.

Li Chi knew that he had won, but he did not sleep that night in his anxiety that something might go wrong. The high officials arrived at nine the next morning, and they were closeted with Tzu for almost three hours. When they left to freshen themselves for lunch, Tzu came to the door. Li Chi was waiting, and Tzu handed him a letter. Li Chi read it carefully. His heart was pounding but he hid his delight. "It seems in order," he said. "You'll have no trouble from the villagers. After the inspectors go, I'll give you some documents I'm sure you'll be glad to have."

Later that afternoon, Tzu's eyes bulged almost out of his head when he read the letters Li Chi gave him. At first he couldn't seem to believe what they said. Finally, Li Chi showed him the letter he had written to the factory manager, and the reply. Understanding dawned at last in the cadre's pinched face, and with it, finally, belief. The little man seemed suddenly to come alive. He actually laughed aloud, and for a moment Li Chi thought that the cadre was going to embrace him.

The word of Li Chi's triumph spread quickly through the village. The air of excitement, and the sudden release of happiness, were felt by everyone, and before the evening was over they began to collect in the hut of Li Chi's father. Even Comrade Liang came, his broad peasant's face glowing. A celebration—a real celebration with all the wine everyone wanted—was planned for the day that Tzu left.

As usual, Li Chi's adorable little niece was sitting in his lap, her finger in her mouth and her eyes turned up worshipfully at him. "Tell me, little one, did you emulate Lei Feng too?"

The child nodded and took the finger from her mouth. "Teacher told us that when Lei Feng went to sleep he dreamed of Chairman Mao," she lisped prettily. "That's what I did. I dreamed of Chairman Mao." She made a face. "That Lei Feng," she said, and added, "I hate his guts."

Even Comrade Liang laughed.

CHAPTER XVI

Red and Expert Lover

In 1964, Li Chi had what was for him a unique romantic adventure. For once he found himself the pursued, instead of the pursuer. The experience unnerved him.

Perhaps one of the reasons he got himself into such an awkward—and dangerous—predicament was overconfidence. Admittedly, he could hardly be blamed for feeling some self-satisfaction over the way he had handled the situation in his parents' village. Upon returning to Wuhu in August, 1963, he began to notice in himself a certain restlessness. Later he decided that the reason was that Wuhu and his job had ceased to offer him adequate challenge. Comrade Ho had all but openly admitted defeat, and now attempted only to maintain peace within the discussion group. In the college itself, Li Chi had obtained all he wanted. Thus he finally came to the conclusion that it was time to make a change, to seek a slightly more stimulating way of life. This was in early 1964.

It happened that the day after he had come to this conclusion, he received a letter from the Peking People's Art Publishing House inviting him to participate in a forum for the purpose of "seeking means of strengthening the ideological content of the traditional annual New Year pictures." There was nothing ominous in the letter; in fact, he had received the same invitation every year since "Red Smoke" had won the prize in Albania. Previously, however, the forum had never sounded interesting, and he had made up some excuse for not participating. What interested him now was not the forum itself but the fact that it would be convened in Hangchow. He had never seen this beautiful resort town, and it occurred to him that living there might be a pleasant change after Wuhu. In Hangchow was a well-known art college, and Li Chi's almost arrogant self-confidence was such that he did not doubt he could obtain a teaching post at this college if he desired. Meanwhile, the forum offered a free—and easy—means of looking over both the town and the college. He wrote to the publishing house and accepted the invitation.

The reply he received came from the Art College in Hangchow where, he was advised, the forum would meet. The letter authorized his traveling expense and gave him necessary information concerning the schedule of meetings and the college dormitory quarters to which he was assigned. Li Chi thought it all sounded very good.

He thought that it sounded even better two days later when he received another letter from the Art College in Hangchow. This one was written by a Miss Pao. It was not quite clear whether she was writing officially or personally. She said that "we here at the college note with much satisfaction" that an artist of Li Chi's renown would be attending the forum as a guest of the college. She implied that the college authorities would be honored to have Li Chi on the faculty. She praised his art work and mentioned, "*I* particularly liked 'Red Smoke.'" From the letter, Li Chi gathered that Miss Pao belonged to the Party and that she assumed he also was a member. This was not odd, because most people did assume that a man of Li Chi's fame would be a Party member. The overall effect of the letter was conventional political enthusiasm mixed with a certain coyness that Li Chi found rather appealing. He began to look forward to the forum, and in his letter of reply to Comrade Miss Pao he was at his most charming.

It was a mistake. He recognized that the moment he saw her at the bus station in Hangchow. She was of formidable size and strength; obviously her coyness had been an unfamiliar and wholly artificial pose that she had discarded the moment she had received his "friendly" letter. She rushed up to him, clamped his shoulder in a vise-like grip, and exclaimed, "Hah! Found you. Recognized you immediately." She drew out of the pocket of her shapeless Party uniform a newspaper clipping and waved it in his face; Li Chi saw that it was the piece that had carried a picture of him and "Red Smoke" several years ago. "Most girls want looks in a man. Hah! Not me. Hate pretty men. It's what's up here that counts"—she jabbed a finger at her head—"and here." She pounded her breast with her fist. Then, with her fist, she punched Li Chi in the neighborhood of his right shoulder; the blow apparently was meant as a gesture of comradely affection, and for Comrade Miss Pao it probably was a light punch, but Li Chi was staggered by it.

Nevertheless, he was altogether so astonished by Comrade Miss Pao that he was able only to murmur the polite formulas of greeting. She wore the clothes and the two short pigtails of a girl-type Party activist. She was a few years older than Li Chi and fully as tall, but she outweighed him by at least a hundred pounds. It was her hearty aggressiveness, however, that confused Li Chi the most. He had been dimly aware that the emancipation of women plus the career opportunities available under the new regime affected some women by stultifying their traditional Chinese type of femininity, but he himself had never been confronted by a case of this malformation.

"Admirable work you've been doing," she was saying as they left the station. "Ideologically advanced perception in connection with glorious task of uniting minority nationalities."

Responding in kind, Li Chi said that he owed what success he had had to his concentration on the glorious thinking of Chairman Mao Tse-tung. She nodded happily in reply, her more than ample jaws, chins, and bosom adding emphasis by also nodding. Despite himself, Li Chi was fascinated. After all, since 1959, fat persons were uncommon in China. The thought occurred to him that what she really liked about "Red Smoke" was the impression of a rich feast that the painting evoked. He wondered what her position was that enabled her to maintain such formidable poundage.

She had pulled out another clipping that she was now waving in his face. He saw that the clipping was from an art magazine of several years ago; it showed all the prize-winning pictures in the group that had included "Red Smoke." "Glorious national achievement that," she said. "You upheld the honor of our glorious country that day in fraternal Albania."

"How unfortunate," Li Chi replied, "that many of the other prize-winning entries came from the revisionist art of the backsliding fraternal nations."

As Li Chi expected, Comrade Miss Pao responded by quivering massively in indignation. "I saw those so-called paintings," she said through clenched teeth. "Vicious, treacherous attempts to sap revolutionary vigor with enticing pictures of peaceful coexistence. One death is not enough for those traitorous so-called artists and their revisionist masters—"

"Still, the paintings of those revisionist artists were reproduced in our own glorious people's publications," Li Chi reminded her, unable to resist the barb.

"Mistaken policies of some semiliterate, semiconscious, lower-level, rightist-leaning editors," she stated. "They should be made to examine their consciences for counterrevolutionary activities."

Increasingly, Li Chi had been having the feeling that Comrade Miss Pao reminded him of someone, and now he knew: Miss Sung in Comrade Ho's discussion group. Miss Sung was as skinny as Miss Pao was fat, but they were about the same age, both had dedicated heart and soul to the Party, and the Communist clichés that made up most of their conversation were identical. Li Chi was saddened by what seemed to him a waste of femininity, and he sighed.

Somewhat to his consternation, his sigh cut off Miss Pao's string of conventional invective and called forth an answering sigh that rumbled up from the great depths of her bulk. Even more disturbing was the fact that, under the pretext of helping Li Chi with his satchel, she slipped her hand over his. Her grip was not hard—in fact it was tender and rather hot—but Li Chi felt shackled by it.

He had reason to feel increasingly shackled during the next few days. Reluctantly, she let him return to his dormitory at night, but she was up waiting, bright and early, for him to leave the dormitory the next morning. Thereupon she did not let him out of her sight for the rest of the day. Even when he attended the forum meetings, she sat modestly in the back of the room, never making any comments herself, but applauding thunderously his occasional statements. Their "romance" was the talk of the college and of the forum delegates, much to Li Chi's embarrassment.

He discovered that Comrade Miss Pao held some kind of administrative position within the college, and for the duration of the forum, at least, she was responsible for the catering. Thus she was able to ensure that Li Chi had all the food he could possibly eat. One evening, she went so far as to send him a midnight snack, which he shared with his three grateful dormitory roommates. The food was wrapped in a red kerchief that, Li Chi learned, was the red scarf of the Young Pioneers; to Comrade Miss Pao, this scarf, which once had been her own badge of group membership, was a precious memento. The gesture of giving this memento to Li Chi in this manner was strongly symbolic and had unmistakable romantic overtones.

The one aspect of Li Chi that had disturbed Miss Pao was the fact that he was not a Party member. When she had learned this, she had been momentarily put off, but she had been able to fix up everything with her Party superiors. "Nothing to it," she informed Li Chi. "You'll get your membership. Should have had it ages ago. I'll help you." Thereafter, massive doses of elementary political doctrine took up the bulk of her conversation and gave her added excuse—as if she needed any—to keep him constant company. What made the whole situation so awkward for Li Chi was that apparently the woman really had had genuine romantic yearnings toward him for several years. As a wholly romantic person himself, Li Chi understood and sympathized with such feelings, and of course Miss Pao's were infinitely flattering to him personally. She regarded his having come to the forum as fate, and she had no doubt whatever that she and Li Chi were intended to face the future together.

She saw the future clearly. Li Chi would remain in Hangchow. He would accept a teaching post at the Art College and soon he would become a Party member. Thereupon, he and she would wed. She would not only see to his health, welfare, and his creature comforts; she would also give him the expert ideological guidance he needed, thus freeing him to concentrate on his art so that he could achieve ever greater artistic triumphs. This picture seemed to bring great delight to Miss Pao, and she was willing to dwell on it endlessly. Unfortunately, however, it was most depressing to Li Chi, and despite the area's incomparable scenic beauty, he was beginning to find it gloomy.

On the fourth day of his visit to Hangchow, Li Chi made his first feeble attempts to break away from the tender chains that slowly but remorselessly were tightening around him. That day, she had led him along some little-used walks through the hills surrounding the scenic West Lake. In a deserted and secluded spot she had leaned against him breastily, breathing hard from the exertion of the climb, and had begged him to allow her to rest. Once seated, Li Chi found himself lost and helpless in her embrace. It must be said, perhaps in criticism of Li Chi, that he was not entirely repulsed by Miss Pao; a certain healthy curiosity, if nothing else, permitted him to participate experimentally in the embrace. His mind was changed quickly, however, by the first ominous stirring of her passion. Suddenly the prospect of facing the full fury of Comrade Miss Pao's unleashed lust filled him with terror. With great effort, he managed to distract her by convincing her that he had some difficult problem on his mind. He permitted her finally to drag it out of him. The problem was, he told her, that he was romantically linked to a woman back in Wuhu. Was it possible to be in love with two women, he wanted to know? And if so, was it decent?

Miss Pao sat up. She was obviously upset—but only for a moment. As she looked at the problem from all sides, she saw with increasing clarity that the situation was still further indication that she and Li Chi were meant for each other. The girl in Wuhu, Miss Pao convinced herself, was some pretty little light-headed thing, immature and ideologically undeveloped. She was completely *wrong* for Li Chi; but, being a man, he lacked good judgment about what was best for him. In the end, however, he would see how superficial his feelings for the Wuhu girl had been when he learned how richly rewarding and satisfying his relationship could be with a girl who could be a real help to him and would unite with him on an advanced ideological level. "Buck up, man," she said to him, giving him another of those affectionate but shattering punches. "You've nothing to worry about."

Li Chi, however, had plenty to worry about. In fact, he was becoming desperate. In lying to Comrade Miss Pao about an involvement with a Wuhu woman, he had been thinking of Miss Sung simply because the two women were spiritually—if not physically—so much alike. Seeking some way out of the predicament, it occurred to him that Miss Sung's presence in Hangchow might somehow relieve the pressure he was enduring from Comrade Miss Pao.

On impulse, he obtained permission to telephone Comrade Ho in Wuhu. He told Ho that he felt strongly that someone from the group should come here "to observe the remarkably fine organization and tremendous achievement of the forum." He reminded Ho that the Peking Propaganda Department cadres attached great importance to the "ideological elevation of the masses" through the medium of the New Year pictures. He pointed out that in Anhwei Province alone, ten million of the pictures had been sold last year. He hinted that the nearby colleges were remiss in not sending observers to the important forum. Without quite saying so, he suggested that the person who *did* get the idea of sending an observer might well come to the favorable attention of high officials who held both propaganda and educational authority. He could almost hear Comrade Ho's enthusiastic thought waves over the wire. Li Chi, however, had almost oversold the idea; Comrade Ho himself was on the verge of taking the next bus for Hangchow. Thinking quickly, Li Chi said that, unfortunately, the available lodging for men had been taken up but that a woman observer could be accommodated. "Comrade Miss Sung will leave at once," Comrade Ho said. "See that you meet her and that the proper authorities are informed that *our* college has sent an observer—"

Li Chi obeyed these instructions, but he also discreetly let it be known that the woman he loved in Wuhu was coming as the observer. The other forum delegates were developing an intense interest in the outcome of Li Chi's affairs.

Two days later, Li Chi accompanied by Comrade Miss Pao met Comrade Miss Sung. Li Chi could tell that Miss Pao expected an attractive younger woman and was determined to take a pleasant, tolerant, but firm upper hand immediately. She was therefore totally unprepared for Comrade Miss Sung, a woman of her own age and of equally formidable ideological achievement.

Comrade Miss Sung was equally unprepared for the encounter. She had had no idea what to expect. The day before, she had been taken suddenly from her files and instructed to go to Hangchow to "observe" the forum. She assumed that she was required in Hangchow for some larger purpose that would be revealed in good time. Meanwhile, she was aware of inexplicable but intense antagonism from the fat Comrade Miss Pao, and she saw that the same Miss Pao was being belligerently possessive about Li Chi.

Miss Sung always jumped quickly to conclusions, and later that same day she jumped to one about her real mission in Hangchow; for once she was not far wrong. She soon heard the gossip that the fat Miss Pao had been pursuing Li Chi shamelessly. She also heard that Li Chi's only defense was a deep, if hitherto hidden, passion for herself. She had been sent to save Li Chi from a designing woman and from himself. The honor of Wuhu Normal was at stake. "Are we going to let these hoity-toity people and their so-called art college take *our* art teacher from us?" she demanded of herself, and answered firmly, "Never!"

The first inkling Li Chi had of Miss Sung's "purpose" came when he received an urgent message from her early that evening to meet her at a certain park near his dormitory. He found her standing alone in the shadow of a tree. "I came as quickly as I could, Miss Sung," he said. "What is it?"

But she did not answer. She stared up at him intensely in the gathering dusk. Suddenly she grabbed his hand. "Ah, my poor boy. My poor, *poor* boy!" she said. She spoke quietly but her voice throbbed with emotion. "To think that all these years, in your heart, you have held these tender, sweet sentiments—"

Li Chi stared at her in amazement and was about to ask her what she meant, but she stopped him with gentle fingers on his lips. "I know. I know what you're going to say," she said. "I was a Party member, ideologically far in advance of you. You were in no position to reveal your feelings. Often—oh, I know I must have seemed heartless, cruel to you—I was forced to make you examine your thoughts and activities to see the political errors."

Again Li Chi tried to speak, but again she stopped him. "Don't apologize," she said. "I've forgiven every mistake you've ever made. Never fear. With my guidance you'll be a Party member before you know it. With my help you will become a great artist, and through our life together we'll contribute invaluably to socialist construction." With that she pulled his hand toward her and pressed it against her wildly beating heart.

Li Chi now was speechless—speechless with horror. He was not sure which fate would be worse—married to Miss Pao or Miss Sung—but he felt that either would be worse than death. Miss Sung accepted that he was overcome with emotion and happiness. She pulled him down beside her and then, to his amazement, Li Chi found himself locked with her in an impassioned embrace. He was not as frightened with her as he was with Miss Pao, but he had a terrifying feeling of being utterly helpless before the merest whims of fate. He wondered dully what would happen to him, and he doubted if it would be anything good. "Don't worry, dear boy, about anything," she finally said huskily into his ear. "*I'll* take care of that other woman—that *creature*."

The next morning, after a sleepless night, Li Chi arrived at the forum meeting, having managed to avoid both women. They arrived soon after; they glared at each other but competed in casting affectionate—and possessive—glances at Li Chi.

The subject being discussed that morning was Chairman Mao's policy of "No courtship—late marriage." Various aspects of this subject had been brought up frequently in the meetings. Traditionally, the New Year pictures were painted in the old style, and depicted dancers, opera stars, warriors, heroes, demons, and especially scenes of home life. Abundant harvests and many children were perhaps the commonest themes representing contentment. Nowadays, however, scenes of abundant harvests would be too bitterly ironic, and the subject was not even mentioned. The family with many children, however, would be a popular subject, but official policy now was late marriage and fewer children. Thus a conflict existed between the public demand and the government policy. In effect, the whole forum was merely another of the Communist façades. Ostensibly, well-known artists and editors discussed what was needed to fulfill the demands of the masses. In one meeting the members gave their various viewpoints; afterward propaganda cadres told them what their views were expected to be, and in the next meeting the members unanimously agreed that the masses wanted most what just so happened to be the Party's policy.

At this particular meeting, the unanimous agreement was to be reached that the New Year's pictures on the subject of family life were to depict only middle-aged married couples who nevertheless had only small children and, at the most, only two. Li Chi took the opportunity, however, to widen the scope of the discussion. Pointing out that most simple people took these pictures very seriously, he stressed the importance that everyone connected with the pictures should live according to the principles expressed in the pictures. This included the artists, editors, publishers, and responsible Party cadres. Thus if the policy was "no courtship—late marriage," then all present were morally obligated to practice it fully and carefully.

He had barely finished when Comrade Miss Pao obtained permission to speak. "It is not marriage itself that our glorious leader is against. It is the distractions of family life and the burdens of many children. Ideologically advanced people know when their marriage is good for socialism or not. I for one have fully prepared myself for a high-level ideological marriage. For example, I have had myself fitted for the proper type of contraceptive device—"

This kind of straight talk, even though expected from a Party activist, caused a gasp among the largely male audience, and

Miss Pao sat down with an air of defiance to the murmur of disapproval.

Miss Sung now stood up. "Some people," she said loftily, "rationalize their own selfish wishes as being the will of the masses and the best policy of the Party. Really forward-looking progressive people in a socialist society, however, obtain expert advice from the proper authorities before taking action. For example, before I decided that I ought to accept a marriage proposal, I spoke to the Party Secretary of an important institution—"

Li Chi groaned aloud. No argument he could devise would change the minds of these women, and they were too adroit for him in their manipulation of official policy to back their arguments. Li Chi could think of only a desperate, last-ditch possible means of evading the fate that seemed inevitably in store for him.

Another subject that was under discussion in the meeting concerned the "emulation principle" and how to project it by means of the New Year pictures. This principle was based on the slogan "Study the advanced, emulate the advanced, learn from the advanced, and catch up with the advanced." A campaign was being waged to implement the slogan. Thus each worker who was not of the advanced type was to try to catch up with and surpass one who was. Each factory was to try to surpass the most advanced factory of its type. And even each city was to try to better the most advanced (Shanghai).

Li Chi now obtained permission to ask a question about this campaign, a question, he said, that he needed the answer to before he could think constructively about the campaign as a subject for pictures.

"I cannot understand how this campaign, which goes from the lowest level of one worker learning from another and reaches to the topmost levels where the city of Nanking learns from the city of Shanghai, can stop short of the international level. Our country, as Chairman Mao has said, is poor and blank. We admittedly have much to learn, much to emulate, much to catch up with. How can we, as part of the socialist camp, stop short of the important international stage of emulating the Soviet Union, learning from the Soviet Union, and catching up—"

He never was able to finish this traitorous question. The assembled delegates shouted him down. The words "rightist" and "deviationist" were heard clearly. When order had been restored, Li Chi was asked to leave, as a disrupting influence. He knew that some sort of disciplinary action would be decided upon and that until then he would not be expected to participate further in the forum but would be expected to stay quietly in his room. He hoped that he had disillusioned the two Party-member women about his political level and that they would now disassociate themselves from any thought of romance with him.

Alas! Li Chi was wrong. An hour later, obviously at the end of the meeting, he received another urgent message from Miss Sung to meet again in the same park. She shook her head sadly at him when he joined her, and despite himself Li Chi felt like a naughty child. "My poor, *poor* boy," she said. "You see? You really do need my guidance badly. But don't worry, all is not lost. The decision was that no action will be taken against you, and no mark will be placed against your brilliant record, but you are not to participate further in the forum." Again she took his hand. "We'll leave this horrid place together—you and I— on tomorrow's bus. I will begin at once the instruction that will prevent you from ever making again the error you made today—"

When she permitted him to return to his dormitory, he realized that a return to Wuhu would mean an inevitable commitment to Miss Sung and a lifelong dreariness in the town that he now realized he never wanted to see again.

Two hours later, Comrade Miss Pao stormed into the dormitory, demanded to see him, and dragged him out. "Bad blunder," she said, referring obviously to his comment at the forum. "But I fixed everything. No black marks on your record. That's the thing, man. A spotless record." She punched him for emphasis this time, rather than for affection. Then she hugged him mightily. "Now do you see how badly you need me?" she asked. She told him that he was to be spoken to by Party Secretary Tu. This was the decision of the forum officials. "Don't worry about it," Miss Pao said. "Comrade Tu is an old man. He'll probably do no more than scold you—"

Li Chi now realized that if he stayed in Hangchow he would face the rest of his life with Miss Pao. He could take his choice. Both prospects filled him with despair

Comrade Party Secretary Tu was indeed old. Li Chi remembered that the man had been on the Long March and once had been a close confidant of Chairman Mao himself. Li Chi was apprehensive of the attitude the old warrior would take.

Tu motioned to him with a palsied hand to take a seat, and studied him for a moment in silence. Finally he said: "Mr. Li Chi, I want to ask if you'll join the Party. No fuss or bother—I still have some influence in Peking—just say Yes, and it will be fixed up."

"There is, I believe, much studying to do," Li Chi stammered. "Long training—"

"Nonsense," Tu said. He made an impatient gesture. "Answer Yes or No."

"Comrade, sir, if you put it that way, I must say No," Li Chi said.

The old man nodded and sighed deeply. "That's what I thought you'd say," he said. "Ever since that Comrade Miss Pao decided you would be her husband, I have been studying your record. It fascinates me, Mr. Li Chi. I admire how you brought in that Miss Sung, pitted the two women against each other, and then ducked out from under both by saying something politically unacceptable."

"I'm sorry about that—" Li Chi began.

But the old man cut him short. "I don't give a damn *what* you said. It was the reason you *said* it that bothers me. Ever since the liberation you've been adapting Party policy to *your* convenience. You won't join the Party because you want to *use* the Party for your personal benefit."

"Comrade, sir, you do me injustice. No one person could possibly do what you said."

"Bah!" Tu replied. He pointed a trembling finger at Li Chi. "Don't try that innocent approach on me," he said. He leaned forward. "If I were ten years younger, I wouldn't rest until you were liquidated." He sighed and seemed to shrink in upon himself. "But I'm old and tired. We're all old and tired, we who started this thing. I just want peace and quiet." He seemed to be talking more to himself, but now he studied Li Chi again. "Young man, how would you like to go Hong Kong, to live the rest of your life in the West? I can arrange it for you, and I'd be glad to do it, glad to get rid of you."

Surprisingly, perhaps, Li Chi was not surprised at the offer, and he knew it was genuine. He thought hard, but finally he shook his head. "I wouldn't know how to adapt to that kind of society. I think I'll be happier and will get along better here."

"That's also what I thought you'd say." The old Communist seemed to sink back once more into his own thoughts. "Maybe it was inevitable," he muttered, "that a breed would develop that was immune to our injection. What would be the use of stamping on one? A thousand more would spring up from the dust." He looked up again at Li Chi. "One thing I do know," he said. "I don't want you around here. I don't care where you go, just so you leave Hangchow."

"I'm afraid I do not want to return to Wuhu," Li Chi said hesitantly.

"Where, then? Come on, man, I don't have all day."

Li Chi knew precisely where he wanted to go. "Lanchow," he said. The old man shrugged, took a paper, and then began quickly to write a letter.

211

A feeling of great relief came over Li Chi. He was aware of a thrill of excitement as he remembered the lovely Hui girl, Ka Lo. Mostly, however, he knew the delight of embarking on a new and exciting life, a life that he did not doubt he could control in all its essential aspects and mold precisely to his own particular taste.

CHAPTER XVII

The Last Word

Unfortunately, I have found no one who has heard what happened to Li Chi in Lanchow. Because Lanchow is where he evidently wanted to go, I feel sure that he got there. (A characteristic common to legendary figures is that they generally get what they want.) Thus I do not doubt that also he found the beautiful Ka Lo and contrived some ingenious method of making the local Party cadres assist him in a renewed romance with her.

The only information I have about Li Chi for the period from mid-1964 to mid-1965 places him, not in Lanchow, but in Huehot, Inner Mongolia. Here, however, he had an adventure so similar to the one described in Chapter VIII, "The Potato Pit," that it does not bear repeating. Li Chi seems to be a composite of several prototypes, one of whom, an artist named Kuo Ti, did spend several years in Huehot. Thus, I believe that, in this case, an anecdote about the legendary Li Chi has become associated with a real person, Kuo Ti—or vice-versa.

Nevertheless, there is a curious Li Chi anecdote—the latest

one we presently have, in fact—that places him in Shantung Province in the latter part of 1965. The anecdote is not exactly typical, but it was told by one of the few people who claim to have had direct personal contact with him. Also, there is mention in the anecdote of the deadly poisonous crimson dye Li Chi had learned to make when he was twelve, the dye with which he had sketched Mrs. Chuan and her lovers. Hence the anecdote has some claim to authenticity.

In any case, in the autumn of 1965, Li Chi was said to be teaching in a Shantung commune's "Half-Work Half-Study" school. Two types of students, apparently, infested these schools. One type included the lazy who wanted to avoid manual labor (the half-study meant that they needed to work only half-days). The other type included indifferent scholars whose parents nevertheless insisted that they get an education (this enabled them to spend only half-days at study.) Neither type included pupils who were likely to benefit from anything Li Chi had to teach.

The one exception was a young man named Tun Tsi-lin. As a child, he had shown exceptional scholastic ability and had been sent to a proper urban school. With the collapse of the Leap, however, he was sent to the commune to work on the land.

Tun had a great-uncle who owned a small business in Singapore; during the period of terrible food shortages, the uncle sent food packages to Tun's family. In most of the country, people who received packages from overseas Chinese abroad did not suffer from too much discrimination. In Tun's area, however, contact with outsiders was so rare that the Tun family came under suspicion. For this reason, young Tsi-lin tried to get permission to leave and join his uncle in Singapore.

This was a bad mistake. He was denied permission to leave and, although no permanent black mark was made on his record, the local cadres treated him as though he had come under bourgeois influence to the extent that he was an "unregenerate unacceptable class element." This forced him to work much harder than everyone else in the attempt to overcome the terrible stigma.

The boy aroused Li Chi's sympathy. Moreover, Tsi-lin had genuine artistic talent. For these reasons, plus the fact that Li Chi had no fear of being "tainted" by the boy's background, he was nice to young Tun. Understandably Tun, who had long been treated as an outcast, responded with much gratitude and warmth.

The Half-Work Half-Study schools were supplied with the absolute minimum of equipment. Li Chi, therefore, had to struggle constantly to find the materials with which to keep his art class going. He resorted to the use of homemade pigments and dyes that he had learned from the old Hui woman in Lanchow. Young Tun often accompanied him on the field trips to look for the plants and clays.

From their talks on these occasions, Li Chi slowly realized that Tun had unrealistic hopes and dreams about his future. Tun would always be blocked by the suspicious cadres, no matter how hard he worked or what he learned. Sooner or later, he himself would realize that his future contained nothing but unending drudgery. When that happened, Li Chi knew that Tun would break in mind and spirit. The only hope for Tun, Li Chi finally realized, was to get away from the China mainland and begin a new life outside.

Thus, for the first time, Li Chi put his mind to the problem of escaping from the country. The problem seemed formidable because Shantung was in the northern part of the country, whereas the only likely escape places were in the South or Southwest. Nevertheless, a germ of an idea began to grow in Li Chi's head, and he was soon at work on the props that his plan, if it proved workable, would require.

A week later, he and Tun were searching for herbs along a riverbank, and they came across some bushes with reddish-brown berries. Li Chi recognized them immediately as the berries from which he had made the poisonous red dye years before in his home village. At the same time the final missing part of his plan fell into place. "Sit down, old Tun Tsi-lin," he said. "I have some serious matters to discuss with you."

Thereupon, Li Chi gently but firmly told Tun that hopes for any kind of reasonable future here were impossible. Subconsciously, Tun had known this, and Li Chi therefore had little difficulty in convincing his friend. Tun's reaction was as bad as Li Chi had feared. The young man buried his face in his hands. "There's no more reason to live," he said. "I'll throw myself in the river—"

"Instead of that, why don't you try for a new life in Hong Kong, perhaps, or in Taiwan, or even in the West?" Tun looked up in surprise, and Li Chi continued. "You think that escape from here is impossible, but look at this and tell me what it is."

Tun took the letter Li Chi offered him; he read it and then looked at Li Chi in confusion. "This is an authorization from you for me to proceed to the commune's headquarters, draw three yuan for travel expenses to the shopping center, where I am to purchase some school supplies—" Tun said.

"And you recognize my handwriting and signature?" Li Chi asked. When Tun nodded, Li Chi continued. "Would you have any hesitation about taking this trip with that authorization?" This time Tun shook his head. "In that case, why should you have any hesitation about forging your own travel authorization?"

A light began to dawn in Tun's face. "You mean," he asked in a hushed voice, "I should travel all the way across this country and *out* on documents I forge as I go along?"

"It's not so difficult as you think," Li Chi said. "I've moved all around this country legitimately, and I always thought that I could make more authoritative-looking travel documents than the ones I was carrying." He now handed Tun a dozen or so additional letters. "Here are some I've made that I swear will give you a good fast start," he said, and added, "Use my legitimate letter to get you off the commune. At the shopping center use the others to get you going westward."

"But won't someone check on me?" Tun asked.

"If someone checks the letter signed by me, I'll confirm it. But why should anyone bother checking a reasonable-sounding travel permit that amounts to only a few yuan?" Li Chi asked. "No one ever checked any of my travel authorizations, and they were far more complicated than these."

Tun was becoming excited. "Do you really think this will work?" he asked.

"Never write out a voucher for a large sum," Li Chi said. "Learn the names of at least two people in every place you go to so that you can use them as references in the next place. Change your name after every two or three jumps. Move steadily, but don't be in a rush. I don't think you'll have any trouble."

Tun jumped up and began to pace back and forth. "I would stick to the back routes, not the main ones," he said. "That way, I would be dealing with only the lowest cadres. They have been so beaten down by the recent campaigns against government graft that they wouldn't dare interfere with someone who seemed to be on official business."

Li Chi nodded. "Your big advantage is that you're smarter than the average official you'll deal with," he said. "The secret of the regime's control is the system of each person watching his neighbor, but the system doesn't work for a person without neighbors, a person on the move."

"I could leave tonight—right now—if I wanted to!" Tun said.

"One small but important detail remains," Li Chi said. He stood up and brushed dirt off his hands. "Your death," he added. Tun blinked in surprise, and Li Chi explained: "Once you're moving, no one you meet is likely to check back on you, but the authorities *here* might make an effort to trace you if you just disappeared. You'll be spared that if they think you're dead."

Tun laughed. "You've thought of everything," he said. "Have you planned a suitable end for me?"

"You are to die from a poisonous paint we're going to make now," Li Chi said. "And you'll have to be very careful or it really will kill you."

They spent the rest of that afternoon making the crimson dye. Thereupon Li Chi had Tun paint a picture with it. Finally, on the riverbank, they planted the evidence for what would appear to be Tun's death. The evidence indicated that Tun had returned to make another small pot of the dye and that he had probably spilled some of the poison on himself; tearing off his shirt, he had run to the river to wash the poison off; he had been overcome, however, had fallen in and had been washed away.

That night, Tun told his family that he would be leaving; the fact was to be a secret, but his family was not to believe any news about his death. He left his house several hours before dawn.

Li Chi meanwhile was preparing an exhibition that would be the contribution from his class to a school celebration in honor of Wang Chieh. This person was the latest in a long series of heroes that the Chinese Communist propagandists had created and that the Chinese people were meant to emulate. Lei Feng had been typical of the type; he had found great joy in hunger, privation, self-sacrifice, hard work, and worship of the Party and Chairman Mao, and these were qualities that the authorities wished the masses to acquire. Wang Chieh, however, was a fierce and fearless warrior. He also found joy in hunger, hardship, and discomfort. Unlike Lei Feng, however, Wang Chieh was really happly only when he was slaughtering the enemies of socialism in great numbers. At twenty-three, Wang had become a demolitions expert. One day, he saw that a pile of dynamite was about to explode; he threw himself on top of the pile and thereby saved the lives of twelve comrades. Apparently, the authorities expected war on a large scale in the near future and were trying to imbue the masses with the necessary spirit of aggressiveness and self-sacrifice.

In any case, Tun's picture, painted with the poisonous dye, illustrated Wang Chieh's tragic end. Li Chi's other pupils presented crudely drawn PLA men and typical slogans, such as "Honor Wang Chieh; emulate him," or "Undaunted by Hardship—Unafraid of Death." Tun's picture, therefore, was quite special, and stood out dramatically from the others.

The Party Secretary of the school glanced at it, turned away, shook his head as though trying to clear it, and then turned back to the picture slowly. This was three days after Tun had left, and the day before the Wang Chieh celebration. "This is a *hand!*" the Party Secretary said, pointing to a bleeding hand that was exploding off to the left in a burst of flame. "Comrade Art Teacher, I'll have you know that in this school, degenerate bourgeois abstractionist revisionist so-called art will not be tolerated."

"Absolutely not!" Li Chi said, as indignantly as he could.

"Yes, hm-mm," the Party Secretary said, and leaned closer to study the picture. "Here is a *foot!*" he exclaimed, and then drew back with a shiver of distaste. "This was painted by young Tun, I see. Revolting bourgeois influences plainly visible. This picture, Comrade, is an insult to our national hero." He glanced at Li Chi. "At three this afternoon, you will report to a special meeting of the commune authorities. Bring this vile picture and the incorrigible hooligan who painted it."

That afternoon, however, Li Chi revealed Tun's tragic accident. The boy's family seemed grief-stricken, but Li Chi knew that they were only acting. Tests were made on a bit of the dye that remained in the broken pot, and it was proved that the dye was indeed poisonous.

Because of all the excitement, the special meeting did not convene until late that evening. The Party Secretary of the commune spoke first. "I know that we are all unhappy about the unfortunate accident," he said. "But we are here to decide upon the suitability of this rather startling picture. Does it belong in our exhibition honoring our great hero Wang Chieh?"

Li Chi arose immediately. "That picture," he stated, "will honor not only Wang Chieh. It will bring lasting fame to our commune."

"I condone this emphasis on death," the school's Party Secretary said. "We honor Wang Chieh's great *spirit* of sacrifice, but *this*—all these arms and legs flying about—it's . . ."

". . . it's socialist realism," Li Chi interrupted. "Our great Chairman Mao himself told us to strive for socialist realism. Here, in Tun's masterpiece, we perceive something of the sacrifice Wang Chieh made for us." Li Chi's audience shuffled restlessly and there were a few mutters of protest, but he pushed on. "Tun, our young comrade, is gone, but he has left for us a veritable monument. In painting that picture, he sacrificed himself just as nobly as did Wang Chieh—"

At this, there were cries of indignation. The commune Party Secretary even implied that Li Chi was insulting the national hero.

Li Chi waited calmly until the talking stopped. "Young Tun knew how dangerous the dye was," he said then, "but to him only that dye was the proper shade of revolutionary red and was lasting enough to honor the hero adequately. We talk about how *we* will honor Wang Chieh, but young Tun sacrificed his own life in order to make us understand the extent of the hero's sacrifice."

The audience was silent now, and Li Chi could see that the officials at least were considering the situation from his viewpoint. "We don't want to disparage young Tun," the school's Party Secretary said, "but an artist should know the dangers of his own trade. Wasn't he just an ordinary youngster who made a foolish mistake?"

"Lei Feng certainly was ordinary and he was even younger," Li Chi said. "He was killed when his own truck was backed into a pole. Was he foolish? Wang Chieh was also ordinary, and he was no older than Tun. As a demolitions expert he knew the dangers of his trade. Yet he was blown up by some of his dynamite. Was he any smarter than Tun?" There were no further arguments, and Li Chi now introduced the point that he knew would have the most effect. "Wang Chieh, a national hero, came from Shantung and thus brought prestige to our province. If Tun, whose sacrifice was no less noble, should be given national recognition, think of the prestige this commune would acquire."

A gasp came from the audience, and then silence. Suddenly the school Party Secretary stood up. "Long live Tun Tsi-lin!" he shouted. In the next moment everyone was cheering.

"Don't get too close to the picture," Li Chi warned them. "Remember that it is dangerous. . . ."

Those who create the national heroes in Communist China are jealous gods; they put up with no competition. They certainly were not going to allow a crazy artist and a few idiotic commune cadres to play around with creation. Thus Tun remained a hero only in the commune. Li Chi was aware that this would happen even if the commune cadres were not. Nevertheless, the cadres, in their attempt to make young Tun a national hero, were forced to remove all stigma from the Tun family; in fact, as relatives of the hero, the family was even given a certain amount of respect and privilege.

All this (and Li Chi's generous efforts) were revealed in a long, carefully written letter sent by the elder Tun to the relative in Singapore.

Young Tun made the trip to Hong Kong in about seven weeks. Apparently he had many adventures but no real difficulties. In Hong Kong he had a hard time, but he finally managed to get in touch with the Singapore uncle, who immediately arranged to bring the young man there. The uncle also was able to inform the family in Shantung that the boy had arrived safely.

It is typical of the Li Chi legend that he should be credited

221

with the plan to travel across Communist China and escape from the country on forged letters. This method of escape, however, is not uncommon. In fact, there is evidence indicating the possibility that an unknown number of people in Communist China live by forging travel orders and expense vouchers. They keep on the move constantly, and the nomadic life must be lonely, but apparently, for some people, it has its compensations.

Such people have learned to survive by exploiting a deficiency in the Chinese Communist system, but they have nothing in common with Li Chi. He has learned to *thrive* by exploiting the contradictions within the Chinese Communist ideology. He grows stronger and more secure as the contradictions increase and become more glaring. He probably represents the single most dangerous threat to China's present regime.

That threat, of course, is nothing more than the inherent and indestructible good sense of the Chinese people.

DATE DUE			